A Sip of Cerasee Tea

A Sip of Cerasee Tea

Taking the BOLDEST STEPS

S.E. WILLIAMS

First published in Jamaica 2019
by
S. E. Williams
Sweet Wally Productions
Suite #3, 3 West Arcadia Avenue
Kingston 5, Jamaica
E-mail: asipofceraseetea@gmail.com

ISBN: 978-976-8277-45-9 (paperback)
978-976-8277-46-6 (ebook)

A catalogue record of this book is available
from the National Library of Jamaica.

Cover design by Rory Brown
(email: rpbrown2016@gmail.com)

Book design by Robert Harris
(email: roberth@cwjamaica.com)
Set in Centaur MT 13/16 x 21

Printed in the United States of America

Dedicated to my mother who always believed in me,
even when I forgot to believe in myself.

Contents

Preface

A Sip of Cerasee Tea: Taking the Boldest Steps explores themes of trust and perseverance. Based on actual events, it chronicles the experiences of a Jamaican woman, Sanaa Wallenston, while growing up in Jamaica during the country's most dramatic socio-political period in the late 1970s.

The story provides an intimate look into Sanaa's inner struggles to understand the changes she experiences after her father goes missing in 1978. Feeling a grave sense of abandonment, she copes with this loss by burying her memories of her father, avoiding any situation that would require her speaking about him to friends or even to other family members.

As she matures, Sanaa becomes very aware of two strong forces that would overshadow her adult life – love and politics – but she soon becomes wary of both, as neither meets her expectations. While never actively participating in politics, she recalls that her father's last words were that political uncertainty had ruined his business. This fuelled her curiosity to understand how the politics he spoke of was intertwined in the lives of ordinary Jamaicans.

Sanaa's personal journey is juxtaposed against Jamaica's political trajectory and, through her watchful eye, we witness Jamaica – though admired for its culture and outstanding personalities – careening through 30 years of trial and error in governance.

A Sip of Cerasee Tea reinforces the adage that we are not defined by our circumstances. Sanaa rejects the labels that would have repressed her and, despite setbacks, she triumphs by taking bold steps towards her purpose.

Acknowledgements

HEARTIEST THANKS TO ALL THE INTERESTING people who have come into my life, even for brief time spans, as they taught me valuable lessons at important stages of my journey. I also acknowledge those whom I have never met, but whose wise words support the story's underlying themes.

"Maybe coming clean is the ultimate selfish act. A way to absolve yourself by hurting someone who doesn't deserve to be hurt. . ."
(Cindy Chupack, Sex and the City [Season 3: Episode 12], "Don't Ask, Don't Tell" 2000)

"Your time is limited, so don't waste it living someone else's life. Don't be trapped by dogma – which is the result of living with other people's thinking. Don't let the noise of others' opinions drown out your own inner voice. And most importantly, have the courage to follow your heart and intuition."
(Steve Jobs, American Investor and Co-founder of Apple Inc., May 25, 2009)

"We have come to see that half-hearted measures will not work here. We must act on a wide front, consistently and energetically, without failing to take the boldest steps."
(Mikhail Gorbachev on Perestroika, 1987)

I would also like to acknowledge published sources of information consulted, both local and foreign, including *The Gleaner; Jamaica Journal; Jamaica Observer; The Washington Post; The Kerr Report;* Ministry of Education policy papers; Caribbean Policy Research Institute publications; writings from the late Professor Carl Stone and Professor Anthony Harriott, and speeches from former Prime Ministers of Jamaica and the websites of political parties.

To protect privacy, names have been changed, except for those of public figures mentioned. Some timelines in the story have also been compressed.

Interchange between use of Jamaican dialect and Standard English in the dialogue is intentional and consistent with 'code-switching', according to speaker and setting.

prologue

Epiphany

"WELL, WELL, WE FINALLY MEET!" LINCOLN said, his eyes searching my face for family resemblance.

"And I feel like I know yuh for years," I chuckled, hugging him.

Simone chimed in, "Yes man, Wordsworth Wallenston blood strong, so wi must feel like wi know one another long time."

It was about six o'clock on the evening following Independence Day, August 2009, when they came by my apartment to pick me up for dinner. This was the very first time I was going to be spending quality time with my two new siblings, Lincoln and Simone. I was looking forward to our time together . . . looking forward to the opportunity to fully understand my family and who I was.

Simone I had met recently; but Lincoln, I had only spoken to on the telephone a few times prior to this meet-up. Lincoln was neat. I liked him instantly. He slightly fit the picture that I had conjured up in my head when I first spoke with him. I noted that he looked like our father but, like my brother Gary who I grew up with, Lincoln had not inherited the height from our dad.

"Lincoln, let's go by Devon House first . . . yuh can check out the gift shops there for what yuh want to take back home," Simone suggested.

"And we can have some ice cream too!" I snickered.

We continued joking as we headed out. Devon House, a central park in Kingston, was one of my favourite places to visit when I needed some quiet time. It serves as a neutral meeting spot for many, boasting a variety of shops and restaurants. Upon entering the property, you instinctively feel at ease. But this evening it was different for us. The hush of the property magnified the unspoken memories of our father, the unseen member in what was really a party of four.

We headed straight for the popular Devon House ice cream shop. Simone and I already knew what flavour ice cream we wanted, but Lincoln noted the many options available and found it difficult to choose. The variety of ice cream flavours became an extended topic of discussion, even after we received our cones. But this was a useless attempt at avoiding our thoughts about our father, as we sat tightly together on one of the courtyard benches dissecting and savouring our delicious, ice cold dessert. We licked our cones with an unnecessary intensity, and, as we watched the courtyard pigeons picking at the ground for pastry crumbs, I could tell we were each contemplating how sharing this experience would have been while growing up.

After the ice cream, without a word, Lincoln led the

way as we visited some of the shops that sold art and other Jamaican keepsakes.

"If yuh don't see anything here we can also go to the shopping mall just down the road." Simone advised.

"Ok, sisters, let's see." Lincoln chuckled.

After browsing the shops and picking up a few gifts, Lincoln asked, "You girls ready to have a proper dinner now?" The ice cream was great, but I still feeling *peckish!*"

Simone and I laughed – it was obvious that our brother was not yet ready to end the exceptional time he was having with us. We stopped briefly at The Mall in the shopping centre nearby after leaving Devon House but did not stay for long as they were closing for the day. So, my new brother, new sister and I headed to TGI Fridays – where the lights are bright, the music is upbeat, and the air is always festive. There, we assumed, the atmosphere would ease our weighty thoughts and we would have a good time, while I would get to know them better.

We assumed wrong.

No setting could stop our compulsion for comparing our bottled-up feelings for our father. We ordered our meals and, with nothing to do but talk until the food arrived, the urgency of the moment could not be denied. Our souls seemed to merge as finally, each of us took turns to speak, carefully outlining what our lives were like with and without him. Tales recounted rang familiar, yet I was amazed at how much we did not know about the man we called father.

"So, Sanaa, have yuh ever heard your father sing?" Simone asked. "When yuh go to church with him, him sing louder than everybody else – and not to mention offkey."

At this point both Simone and Lincoln were laughing so hard that I could not keep myself from laughing too at the thought of my very stiff father singing.

"No," I said, "I didn't even know that he used to go to church!"

"Well, he didn't go that often," Simone said, "but when him was there, him make sure everybody know!"

Our laughter rang out in the restaurant, but our underlying pain remained hidden from its patrons. My brother and sister continued recounting the tales of growing up Wallenston.

My father was a big disciplinarian and Lincoln, who was a troublesome boy growing up, very often felt the brunt of our father's remedies for bad behaviour.

Lincoln grimaced at the memory.

"After Mommy and him separated, we went to live with her mother. Anytime he would come to visit I gone hide as I was afraid him going to find a reason to beat mi – whether or not mi did misbehave that day!"

The thought made us sober up again. We all had experienced our father's harshness in our lives.

As the evening and tales wore on, I learnt that I had a lot in common with my siblings. Mainly, I learnt that we all shared a similar disconnection from our father while we were growing up because he never knew how to demonstrate love – but, we concluded, he must have loved us in his own strange way. Most of all, I learnt that as grown-ups what we felt for our father was mainly sympathy, but we also felt some regret for the pathos that he had so effortlessly injected in all our lives when we were young. We spoke about the things he did for us and did not do for us and bemoaned the fact that he never at any time had us all together with him.

The closest all of us had ever been together and in proximity to our father at the same time, was upon his death, when his picture appeared in the obituary section of the island's leading newspaper, *The Sunday Gleaner.* There we all were, my siblings and I, with our names lined up, one behind the other under his picture, as if we were one big happy family, when some of us were still virtually strangers to each other.

Our meals arrived but remained untouched for a while.

There was an awkwardness about our emotions and food was the last thing we wanted. In that moment, we wanted to cry the tears we should have collectively shed at the time of his death but could not.

"That man was so hard on me," Lincoln finally said. "For all the beatings I received, I made double the effort to make him proud of me, even as an adult, but I'm not sure it was enough. . ."

There was a noticeable crack in Lincoln's voice as he spoke of our father. Our eyes watered – but we did not know how to handle crying together. We needed to break that somber moment, so I tried to lighten the mood.

"Pass the potato skins, please . . ." I said to my sister, as I blinked away annoying tears.

Simone, who had spent more time around our father than Lincoln or I had, started telling stories about some relatives who I had never met and who Lincoln barely knew. There was my father's brother, Uncle Dermott, who had been in the army. His daughter, Maxine, had spent a few years living in the same house with Simone. Uncle Dermott and our father used to have some deep conversations when they met up at the house; no one could tell what these talks were about as the brothers always spoke with lowered voices. However, there were times when the conversations would escalate into heated discussions, then end suddenly. The next day, they would be friends again, laughing and joking, as brothers should.

Though we laughed at the funny stories about our father, the residual grief made our laughter seem forced. Learn-ing about one's family history in a quick-service restaurant is perhaps not the norm, but for me it was the perfect opportunity to switch on the light on what was once a blackout in my life.

When I went to bed that night, I could not sleep. It was as if all the details of my mummified adolescence and subsequently, disjointed life, came flooding through my brain. This unexpected experience of belatedly mourning my father's death meant reliving the 26 years of my life between 14 and 40. That night I went back in time and passed through bitter memories to empty solitude. I had to relive these memories before I could begin to experience freedom from the bondage of my suppressed past. It was all very overwhelming. In the wee hours of the morning, I jumped out of bed. I had to get rid of the thoughts about my father, infiltrating my mind. The only way to do so was to put them on paper. It was time to face my epiphany.

This is how I took the first step on my journey to understanding who I was. It was like taking a sip of cerasee tea – not pleasant tasting, but good for me, guaranteed to cleanse me of any traces of umbrage I had left in my system.

Once again, I was a young adolescent, for that was when my carefree life ended.

Let me tell you how it all happened.

1

Simple and Unspoilt

MY PERSPECTIVE OF THE WAY THE world works may have been completely different were it not for the series of amazing events that unfolded to interrupt my sheltered life as a teenage girl. Before then, I had a secure and reasonably blissful life. Initially, it was splattered with one recurring childhood fantasy that my dad would come to live with us – my mother, older brother Gary and me – and make my life complete. But that never happened.

I have very little memory of my father in my formative years. His presence in my life seemed steadier after we moved from the house with the patterned glass front door, situated off Hagley Park Road.

My best knowledge of my father's life was of him living in Montego Bay on the western end of the island, where he operated his business. It seemed as if I could never get enough of him. When I was old enough to write intelligibly, I would write to him often, and each evening on my way home from school I would hope that there would be a letter from him waiting for me. It was particularly pleasurable to receive these letters during the summer-time. I would run out to collect them personally, taking my cue from the community postman's ringing bell and the neighbourhood dogs yelping as they tried to outrun his bicycle. This heralded the arrival of my father's letters, fully decorated with his sprawling handwriting.

My father was my favourite person when I was a child. I knew no one else like him. He seemed structured and in control of everything – as if he could singlehandedly fix anything that went wrong around him. He was tall and imposing, very dark in complexion but not particularly handsome. He had a round head, a broad, flat forehead, like that depicted of an Arawak and narrow eyes. His nose was neither large nor small – just managing to fit within the proportion of his other features and avoiding an unattractive finish to his face. His lips were thin, and his teeth would have been perfect were it not for the stains they bore from his nicotine habit.

He and my mother seemed to be complete opposites, both in appearance and disposition. Mom was petite, of a much lighter skin tone, with bolder features. She had a kind face with a ready smile and expressive almond-shaped eyes. Her nose flared elegantly at the nostrils and her lips were soft and full. Mom was unassuming, but she was no push-over. She had a knack for making people fall in love with her once they met her because she was very kind-hearted.

Another difference between my parents was the fact that my father had been educated up to the tertiary level; but my mother had only elementary level education. When she received a half scholarship to attend a technical high school, her mother was unable to afford the balance of the cost and was also quite concerned about sending her only child, a girl, to a school deep in the city of Kingston. Mom had to continue attending the elementary school close to home and her formal education terminated at age 15.

Even so, she was very sharp and could quickly assess situations and the people around her. She could always be relied on to give sound advice and this made her well respected and sought after by her peers and even younger persons. Another important difference between my parents was that my father was financially independent, he had his own business, while my mother had a low-income job as a cashier in a drugstore in downtown Kingston. In fact, Mom had two jobs because at night she would sew for her friends. From this extra income, after paying the bills, she could stretch the funds to buy me storybooks and send me to piano lessons.

Physically, I was a blend of both parents, with my distinguishing features being my mocha complexion and the uneven dimples in my cheeks. While growing up I was not clear on what personality traits I had inherited from my father, but it was evident to me that I had the compassionate nature of my mom.

However, the most significant difference between my parents that mattered was that, while my mom was always home with me, I had only a visiting dad.

I loved my mother, but I was fascinated with my father. When I was little, I spent much of my free time just willing him to come and take me for ice cream and for long rides in his fancy car. And perhaps, I would wish, too, that we could all pile into his car on a Sunday afternoon – Mom, Gary and I – and go for a drive to nowhere in particular. But as I grew a little older and started high school, I realized that none of those dreams would ever materialize. My life was with my mother.

When I was a little girl in primary school, one-on-one time with her involved going shopping downtown – King Street, mainly. She would buy my schoolbooks at Sangster's Book Store then hop into stores like Ammar's for fabric to make my school uniforms or dresses for me to wear to church. Sometimes she would shop for household items at a store called Elite. After a while these trips were no longer very exciting, but I looked forward to this quality time with my mother at least a few times each year. I found her methodical approach to these duties admirable.

Apart from her shopping, Mom did not have much of a social life. She simply did not have the means to take time off to splurge. Her priority was always about working and taking care of us. Mom's only non-work activity was taking us to visit her parents from time to time. More often, they came to visit us. Once or twice a year, she also took us to her friend, Carmelita, for dinner on special holidays like New Year's Day.

Carmelita was a very joyous person. She and my mother

had known each other for years before I was born. Their mothers had also been close friends. Occasionally, whenever she extended an invitation, Mom would allow me to sleep over at Carmelita's. Carmelita was of Cuban and Jamaican descent; her mother was Jamaican, and her father was Cuban. She had a big family of five daughters and a son, ranging in age from toddler to teenager.

Carmelita lived with her husband, mother-in-law and children in a nice middle-class house with a big yard, in Constant Spring. They had a car and a full-time household helper who lived with them. There was no shortage of things to do when I went over to Carmelita's house. The children had a swing in the backyard, a doll's house and a dog that was constantly in the middle of our activities with his playful antics. Carmelita's middle daughter, Camellia, was my best friend. She would sweetly ask her mother to ask my mother, whenever they dropped by, to let me come over to their house to play and spend some time with them. But, by the time I got to the house, Camellia would, very often, be bossy with me; I would threaten to go home and she would become her sweet self again.

Mom and Carmelita had a deep connection that I find hard to describe . . . maybe sisterly. Whatever it was, it kept them in each other's lives – it seemed nothing could come between their mutual respect, if not love, for each other. Mom had no immediate siblings around. Except for her parents and two uncles, she hardly ever saw her handful of relatives. Her half-sisters lived in New York, while her half-brother settled in sunny Tampa after studying in England and Canada, but she never travelled to the United States (US) to visit with any of them. She had only been on Girl Guides' camping trips outside of Kingston in her early youth. Perhaps this was why Carmelita was so dear to my mother, as she took the time out to be a part of our lives, providing some familial warmth to Mom.

I too felt that sense of family with Carmelita. Whenever I spent time at her home, she always made me feel special and I often pretended that I was one of her children. I loved my family; I just liked the fact that my friend Camellia had a mother and father right there, under the same roof with her, plus siblings to play with all the time. For me, that was the true picture of what family meant.

I was safe in my youthful naivety.

I constantly felt alone as a small child, but my life became more interesting when Brenda came to stay with us before we moved from Hagley Park. I was about 5 years old. Brenda was a trueborn country girl from rural Clarendon. She had come to Kingston to learn the art of dressmaking from Mom. Though she was fully literate, Brenda had no skills apart from cooking and housekeeping. She was 17 years old and wanted to be more than a housekeeper, but opportunities for work were lacking in the rural parishes in Jamaica. Brenda arrived at our house with a small, brown suitcase. She seemed innocent and unfettered when she moved in with us that Sunday afternoon. No one could tell that this was her first time at our home; she breezed through the front door as if she had been there before and knew her way around. Without pausing, she headed for a wicker chair under an open window in our living room, while still being introduced to us by my mother's friend, Rupert.

"Town hot eeh? Mi don't know if mi can give up country fi' town yuh nuh!" she exclaimed in her country dialect.

Mom beckoned to Gary, "Bring the fan, Gary. It's in the room."

We did not have an electric fan; but our Chinese-made paper fan would have to cool down our new household member. Notwithstanding the heat, Brenda adjusted to Kingston quickly and fit into our family easily, making our lives more interesting with her stories about country life.

She often told Gary and me how good things were for us compared with where she grew up.

"Bwoy oh bwoy, the amount of goat mi had to tie out to graze bush before going to school every morning," she paused, "Then of course after school, mi and Timmy have to go for dem in the bush and tek dem home," Brenda shook her head before continuing, remembering her tribulations.

"One big goat name Rex decide one evening that him not coming home wid mi and Lord Jesus, him escape and mi had to run for miles and climb down a gully to get him back. Yuh know how much beating I would get if I never find back that goat? Lawd help mi! But thank God mi get him back and Papa did curry him next Labour Day!"

As usual, she suddenly erupted in laughter, which seemed to come up from deep within her belly in her short, stout frame. The story about the runaway goat was funny. But most times we were never sure what Brenda was laughing about – perhaps now that she was living in Kingston, even though in a simple setting, she found the variances between town and country life a ridiculous contrast.

Nothing seemed to bother Brenda. She walked around the house barefooted every day in her boxy clothes and remained unaffected by the troubles of Kingston.

I cannot remember ever seeing her stitching anything on the sewing machine. It seemed Brenda was not keen on sewing, so Mom did all the cutting and stitching, and Brenda put the finishing touches on the clothes – hemming them and trimming the hanging threads.

Brenda was like a second mother when Mom was away at work and her contribution to my young life was invaluable. She would prepare the evening meals and ensure that I did my homework before nightfall. She was like a helpmate for my husbandless mother. Each night before we went to bed, she made sure she knew the order of the next day.

"Ms Mullings, what yuh want mi cook tomorrow?"

"Brenda, yuh know yuh can cook whatever yuh want to cook," Mom would always reply.

This is how it went each night.

About a year after Brenda came to live with us, I got a new little brother.

After years of being my mother's last child – her *wash-belly*, I was happy for this baby brother, but he was not Mom's birthchild – he was Brenda's son. Yes, Brenda had a baby while living with us.

His conception had come as a surprise to everyone – and apparently Brenda too.

"Brenda," I overheard Mom saying to her one morning about two months after she had returned from a long weekend break. "Yuh don't seem too well for a few weeks now and yuh putting on some weight in the middle section. What is really going on with yuh?"

"I not sure yuh nuh Miss Mullings; yuh right, I not feeling so good."

"Brenda, I think I know what it is; and I just going to wait until yuh feel up to telling mi."

"Alright Miss Mullings," Brenda had replied. She seemed detached from the situation.

Mom went to work and nothing more was said about the matter.

Soon I found out that Brenda was expecting a baby and, months later, she gave birth to a beautiful baby boy. We called him Tony.

I remember when Tony was born. We were still living in Hagley Park. Mom had sent me to the verandah when a lady, who I eventually found out was a midwife, arrived.

"Hurry, hurry this way!" Mom said, as I saw her guiding

the bustling old lady with the large bag into Brenda's room.

There were some muffled screams from Brenda and I heard the lady with the bag asking, before they closed the white plywood door,

"How long since she labouring?"

"A couple hours now," Mom said, "but is not time yet, so we were watching it."

Then their voices were drowned out by Brenda's moaning behind the door. I was unaware of what was happening for about an hour until the lady with the bag emerged from the house, saying to Mom,

"Give her some porridge and make sure she breastfeeds the baby."

"Alright, thank yuh very much," Mom said and gave the lady an envelope before she left. Only then was I allowed back into the house and into the room to see Brenda. Mom was beaming but Brenda looked tired and had a swaddled, bawling baby in her arms.

The baby stayed with Brenda until he was a few months old and both she and Mom fussed over him. Then, one Saturday, Brenda took him to Morgan's Pass and left him there with her one of her sisters.

Less than a year after Tony's birth, we moved from Hagley Park. The owners of the house were selling the property. We moved about four kilometres north-east of the Edwardian clock in Half-Way-Tree into a tiny flat across from what would be our new place of worship, Elim, a Brethren church, on lower Shortwood Road. This was off

Constant Spring Road, a major road 'up-town'. Our new home was on the outskirts of where my mom had grown up with her mother in Grants Pen, a poor community bordering the upscale areas of Norbrook and Cherry Gardens. The flat we moved into was much smaller than the house we had left behind. Tucked away in an inconspicuous commune, it lay humbly on the fringes of Kingston 8 – where the rich and the poor live side by side.

After we settled into our new community, when summer came it was Brenda's idea to take Gary and me to her home in Morgan's Pass, so we could get a taste of country life. As she put it, we were growing too 'soft'. Mom reluctantly agreed to send us when I got excited at the idea of seeing Tony. This softened her up. We had only seen him a few times for short spells when Brenda obliged her and brought him up from Clarendon for a week or two.

"OK," Mom said. Please to bring him up with yuh when yuh coming back!"

Brenda laughed but did not reply.

That first trip to the country with Brenda was my first time on a train. I was wide-eyed for the entire journey. I was awed by the breathtaking lushness of the Jamaican countryside, as it glided steadily past us. I was anxious to reach our destination. When we finally disembarked the train, I ran ahead of Brenda as if I had been to her home at some previous time unknown to her. She quickly restrained me.

"Wait nuh Sanaa! Is just a short walk now – wi soon

reach. The house is just around the corner!" Brenda explained.

After what seemed like forever, we finally arrived at the place where Brenda grew up. As I climbed up the incline to my destination, I was met by an expansive, fenceless yard with two houses. To the far end of the yard stood the almost crumbling wattle and daub 'bottom house', built when Brenda's parents first got married. The house looked as if it would topple if even a slight wind blew, but that was where the children and extended family still slept every night and that is where I would sleep during my stay.

It stood out in stark contrast to the more modern concrete 'top house', painted in a cool blue, which Brenda's father, Papa, built just a few years after his wife (whom I never met) succumbed to a terminal illness.

Everything there was green and fresh, simple and unspoilt. Everything seemed perfect.

Well, almost everything.

I shifted my eyes from the foreground of the yard; and right there, in the middle of the green expanse, I was greeted by the gangly naked body of Milton, one of Brenda's nephews, my own age, bathing in a bath pan, right out in the open.

As we walked up closer to him, I expected him to make an attempt to cover himself, but he continued singing and scrubbing, unperturbed as we approached. I was aghast. I had never seen a fully naked boy past the age of infancy. Instantaneously, I learnt that rural folks lived very differently than we did in Kingston – sans modern amenities. There were no modern baths, showers or toilets at Morgan's Pass. In Morgan's Pass I came face to face with nature. However, I did not allow that to put a damper on my spirit.

After my first day, I hated the thought that I would be leaving its serenity and my new borderless playground in a few weeks to return to the pollution and the restrictions of Kingston. Here, I was free to roam – to explore and enjoy the environs, without fear. It was not like home where I was fenced in, though by a protective gate.

On laundry days, Milton and I would go down to Ballads River with Brenda. We would swim in the river and catch *janga* (crawfish) while Brenda sat on the riverbank with the other women of the district, washing in the shallow part of the river. The women would gossip in their textured dialect about the latest happenings in the community, but Brenda was sure to watch me diligently because I was not a swimmer. On other days, our adventure took us to 'mango bush' for bird shooting with some boys from the district. Our home-made slingshots effectively slew the chirping birds we encountered. The day would end with a mango eating contest, where I had the privilege to serve as referee, reminding the boys to stick to the rules of the game, as they tried to outdo each other with tricks.

But Sunday mornings were the best. We were sure to be awoken by the zesty aroma of exquisite chocolate tea brewing in the outside kitchen. For me, this meant that I would not have to partake in the dreadful ritual of choosing my bush tea – fever grass (also known as lemongrass), mint or cerasee, none of which I liked, despite all being lauded for their medicinal properties. All were readily available in five minutes as they grew wild at the side of the bottom house and did not require much preparation. The cerasee was especially good for helping with the colic I got from time to time, after bingeing on the variety of foods I would gobble down, for fear the holiday would run out before I had my fill of them.

Making the chocolate tea however, required a much longer process. Whenever we heard Papa shout our names very early any morning after he had his morning coffee, we knew it was time to help him prepare the chocolate.

"Milton! Sanaa! Yuh wake up?" Papa would shout.

"Yes, Papa!" We shouted back. "Wi coming to help yuh pick chocolate!"

We would dash off to retrieve the pods of cocoa beans that had fallen off the tall cocoa trees in the back of the yard. Afterwards, Papa parched the beans on a piece of zinc over coal fire. When he was ready, he allowed Milton and me to take turns beating the parched beans into a mush, using a heavy wooden stick, in a deep, standing wooden bowl called a mortar. Once the cocoa softened, we would portion it, then roll the small portions into chocolate balls the size of the round part of an 'OK' sign. The balls then sat for days to 'set' the flavour. Though we were so involved in preparing these chocolate balls, we could not have the drink whenever we wished; they were delicacies reserved for making chocolate tea only on a Sunday morning. I would have helped Papa pick cocoa every day if assured just a few sips of this mouth-watering beverage all week, as an alternative to drinking that bitter cerasee tea or the other bush teas.

Most often, breakfast consisted of fried dumplings or just chunky slices of white hard dough bread, bought fresh from Uncle Fred's corner shop at the foot of the hillock, where Brenda's house perched. Sometimes we would have the dumplings or the bread with eggs from the laying hens. The much more 'plucky' roosters that had free run of the yard had no idea that one of them could very well be the protein source for our next Sunday dinner. I hated watching Brenda kill these birds. She would put the flapping body under a pan and one of the men would steady it, then, with a decisive swing of the very sharp machete, Brenda would sever the fowl's head sticking out from the pan.

Our evening meal during the week was easier to prepare. Usually we had either mackerel rundown (mackerel cooked in coconut milk) with boiled dumplings, yams and green bananas or, alternatively, ackee and roast pork with roasted breadfruit and fried plantain, all cooked on a wood fire in the old detached kitchen. We used the rainwater that ran off from the roof of the house to make lemonade – or 'wash' as they called it in the rural areas of Jamaica – and this rounded off our evening meals.

Later, after dark, we played dominoes and card games, straining our eyes in the light provided by the bottle lamps we made by stuffing newspaper soaked in gas oil (the wick) into any empty soda bottle available, and then lighting the exposed end. Of course, the *peeny wallies* (fireflies) flitting around us also made our after-dark recreational activities possible in the absence of electricity. Before bed was the predictable nightcap of *duppy* stories Uncle Timmy, Brenda's older brother, would jokingly tell us. We bravely listened to these scary paranormal tales about community persons who had died but came back as spirits to terrorize their neighbours. I tried not to show how afraid I was of these frightful *duppies* – especially one called Maas Tom. I heard about him the very first night I arrived in Morgan's Pass.

"Brenda, yuh mek the Kingstonian dem know sey Maas Tom *duppy* nuh stop roam the district since him dead? Mek sure dem know dem fi lock the door and all the window dem before dem go sleep every night yuh nuh!" Timmy said this with a frightened look on his face as if he had just seen Maas Tom in our midst.

"So, what going to happen if the windows leave open Uncle Timmy?" I asked innocently.

"Yuh don't want to find out, little town girl. Maas Tom sure going tek out yuh heart mek supper."

Uncle Timmy and the other adults in the yard roared with laughter while I ran into Brenda's arms, afraid. Every night they added on details of incidents where Maas Tom's *duppy* had stolen hearts for supper. But I was determined that that bad country *duppy* would never get to mine.

It was almost impossible to fall sleep after hearing such stories, but we would turn in to bed about 10pm each night to get some rest – a must before another busy day of country life. One thing I did not neglect was checking the doors and windows before getting into bed. Often the crickets, which I never saw but could hear far away in Brenda's backyard, obscured by the thick bushes, punctuated the stillness of the night. They kept me company while I tossed around in the coir bed, trying to find the most comfortable position for a good night's sleep, while praying Maas Tom's *duppy* would not try to steal through the door. Of course, I had triple checked to make sure it was properly locked.

Our next little shake-up came three years later. After living with us and going back and forth between Kingston and the country, Brenda announced that she was returning to Clarendon to get married and settle down in Chapleton. She had reunited with an old boyfriend on one of her visits to Clarendon and he wanted to marry her. Her soon-to-be husband was tired of visiting her in Kingston and wanted her back in Clarendon. That was when Mom said she would adopt little Tony. After all, he was born in our house – right into her hands, Mom reminded Brenda. It was at that stage that Tony came back to Kingston to live with us at my mother's insistence.

"Tony is going on four years old and needs to come up

to Kingston to start school." Mom had said this as if Tony naturally belonged with her.

"Him was supposed to start school down there, yuh nuh," Brenda replied.

"Yes, I know, but he didn't; plus, I can also help him more if he is here with me . . ." Mom insisted. Then she added, as if Brenda needed a better explanation for moving Tony to Kingston to live with her,

"Brenda, Tony's father is abroad and he isn't involved in looking after him. So, yuh don't even need his permission regarding Tony's welfare," Mom ended.

Brenda did not have a rebuttal to that last reason for bringing Tony back. She complied.

"Yes Miss Mullings, yuh right, mi and Tony father not even talking right now; him not coming back to Jamaica at all."

Brenda knew Mom could scarcely afford to take on another child, but she also knew Mom was willing to make the sacrifice for Tony because she loved that delightful little boy so much. And so, Brenda left Tony in Mom's care and went back to Clarendon to get married.

Our visits to Morgan's Pass stopped after Brenda left. Carmelita took up the slack for ensuring I had great adventures, but it was a different type of adventure. Tightly squeezed into Carmelita's old Cortina, we traversed the island, but this time enjoying the resort hospitality offered at the various hotels like Turtle Towers in Ocho Rios and Goblin Hill Hotel in Portland. I appreciated these getaways just as much as I had appreciated being in the natural, rustic ecstasy of Morgan's Pass because I had endless fun in the company of Carmelita's children, nieces and nephew.

All this was before I hit my teenage years – that time in your life when everyone expects you to start acting all grown up overnight. Though the preliminary shift from childhood to adolescence was easy for me, I never stopped dreaming about being a part of what I envisioned to be a perfect family. Up to that time I still had not had any of these fun-type experiences with my mother and my father, and kept wishing for them.

I missed Brenda, but she had given me the best gift possible before leaving – my new brother, Tony. He was the happiest little person I had ever known. He was chubby and had big saucer eyes that popped when he laughed. He warmed Mom's heart with his loving nature, always asking her if she wanted money, as if he realized she was struggling financially. I read stories to him every evening and he listened eagerly. Within one year of coming back to us and starting school, he was reading fluently from his own books and flipping through the pages of our *Grolier Encyclopedia* with heightened interest. I loved having Tony in my life and he loved being the guinea pig for my crazy schemes, all designed to test how much he loved me.

We had lots of fun together, my little brother and I, and today we can look back fondly at the things we did to make each other's life enjoyable.

My mother did not allow my little brother and me to play with the youngsters in the community. Their way of life was different from ours. "The parents don't have them under any regulation", Mom would say. She was a very classy woman, despite limited means.

We had two main options: either we stayed inside the house and watch our black and white TV or read a book, or we could "amuse ourselves" on the verandah, as Mom would say. This could mean using the oblong shaped space to recite Jamaican poetry and sing folk songs – mimicking 'Concert Time' on *Ring Ding*, the beloved local TV show for kids. It was hosted by the folklorist Miss Lou on Saturday mornings, and brought to us courtesy of our single TV station, Jamaica Broadcasting Corporation (JBC TV). On the rare occasion when my godsister Prudence came over, Mom would allow us to play outdoor games like *dandy-shandy* and *stuck-in-the-mud* within the small confines of an imaginary cordoned-off area of the yard, immediately in front of the verandah. That was the extent of our freedom.

We had to be careful not to wander too far on the property at the risk of getting in the way of the landlady and her husband, who lived on the bigger side of the house. Mango season was an exceptionally testing time for us. We would be severely scolded by Mrs Landlady if we were caught picking any mangoes off her prized East Indian mango tree. We therefore had to time the mangoes as they fell off the tree and dash out to pick them up, then make a quick dash back to base (the verandah), much like one would do in a potato race – hoping Mrs Landlady had not heard the thud as the mangoes hit the ground. If she did, even if we did not see her, we would hear her screaming,

"Leave the mangoes dem alone and give somebody else a chance to taste dem! In fact, just pick dem up and bring dem come."

We would have to hand over the mangoes for inspection. If Mrs Landlady felt like being generous, she might allow us to keep the ones that were less than firm. And then she would remind us that greater privileges were extended to us for the Number II mangoes from the tree in the back of the yard.

"Remember yuh can pick as much of those mangoes as yuh like... don't mek anybody stop yuh."

Neither Tony nor I liked Number II mangoes. Phooey.

As I grew into adolescence, the feeling of confinement heightened with the many restrictions I faced. Freedom got even trickier for me when I started high school and outgrew playing and hanging around in the front yard. The only alternative was to spend my time on the open veranda, trying to get some light and air.

I needed an escape.

2

Plunged

IT WAS 1978.

That pivotal year in my life when everything changed.

I was 14 years old and I remember it vividly as it was the same year that marked the beginning of the long eve of political chaos leading to the heated 1980 general election. Some still consider it Jamaica's most crucial election since independence from the British Empire in 1962. It was a time marred with social unrest fuelled by political anarchy and economic downturn. People were questioning the democratic socialist agenda of the 1970s, that had sought to introduce betterment to the Jamaican masses. The distrust was severe. The fear of a *coup d'état* (government overthrow), tinged the upheavals while opposing political groups fought to protect whatever was precious to them.

Everywhere, people – young and old – were afraid they would lose their lives in the crossfire of the opposing factions, and afraid to speak openly about their political persuasion. They were even afraid to wear colours associated with either of the two main political parties – orange or green – as this could get them killed by fanatics defending either side.

At first, I did not understand the cause of all the tension I could feel bouncing off my adult compatriots around me, but I knew it resulted from the politics of the time. In the lanes and crevices of towns across the island, reggae music competed with barking guns. Though the music belted loudly in the streets, it did not erase the feeling of foreboding in the air. Bob Marley and the Wailers' social commentary in their songs throughout the 1970s aptly reflected the realities of the times and the plight of ordinary folks. They declared: "We don't need no more trouble . . . what we need is love."

And Marley was perhaps more passionate about getting rid of the "troubles" than many; not only because he was a peace-loving Rastafarian, but he had survived an assassination attempt nearly two years prior by some who accused him of affiliation with one of the parties. This made him an even stronger peace advocate.

Marley was happy to headline the One Love Peace Concert held at the National Stadium in April 1978, designed to bring everyone together – regardless of party persuasion. But, not even this concert could quiet the sounds of the struggle. Neither did the image of the two leaders of the opposing parties – Michael Manley of the People's National Party (PNP) and Edward Seaga of the Jamaica Labour Party (JLP) – holding hands on stage during this concert end our political friction. Politics was dividing us.

It was like taking a picture of a beautiful family and ripping it down the middle. We became a fragmented nation because of polarizing political ideologies and there would be no piecing us back together for some time.

The democratic socialist policy adopted by the PNP during that period was a double-edged sword. It brought fear because some did not understand its power to improve lives. But it was not a new trend that Michael Manley had dreamed up. He had only reaffirmed and ramped up what was in the PNP Constitution since 1940. His actions considerably altered the country's socioeconomic landscape by narrowing the wide gap between rich and poor. Though the revolutionary policies stirred up conflict in Jamaica, it served to expand the middle-class through the creation of opportunities for the poorer classes to move up the social ladder, primarily through increased access to education and property ownership.

During our break periods at school, we sat under the lignum vitae tree in front of the Old Building at St Andrew High School for Girls, trying to interpret the goings-on that defined our world.

"Socialism simply means that the rich will have to give up their homes to the government and live like the rest of us," one friend said.

"But how can that be?" another asked. "Yuh mean after my parents have worked so hard to build their business and make us comfortable, we will have to walk away from all that?"

This was Alice. She was from a well-to-do family. I could understand her concern.

"But how is that alone going to help us – the not-so-rich?" I asked. "We can't all move into those houses. There has to be a better way of helping the poor."

"Sanaa, the government is helping the poor; that is how people like us are attending this school now," my friend Melody stated. Her family was not exactly struggling – in fact they were also well off, but she was a very practical and empathetic person.

Everyone chimed in that Melody was right. And I agreed. Education was important for the poor, to give us choices and opportunities for a better life. Something did not add up and there were more speculations about the next steps in socialism. None of us knew what was next, as we still were not even sure what socialism meant.

At home, Mom vehemently disputed this notion of the PNP Government taking from the rich to help the poor. Naturally. She was sympathetic to the socialist government of the day – Michael Manley was the son of Norman Manley, Jamaica's Premier before we gained independence from the British Monarchy. Mom had loved 'Father Manley', had admired the work of his wife Edna, a sculptor and trailblazer developing Jamaica's visual arts, and now loved their son who was leading the change for better. As far as she knew, Michael Manley had our best interest at heart and the negative talk about him and his intentions were evil rumours spread by the uninformed. But if things were going in a better direction for the majority, the poor, how was it that everyone was so disgruntled, I wondered.

No one tells you anything when you are a child. All I was sure of was that my life was changing drastically, at 14 years old. I started to experience scarcity of necessities in a real way.

Mom was reticent about this part of the drama, but we saw her shopping bags getting fewer and fewer as the weeks rolled by. The undertones of terror from the political turmoil made the lack all the worse. It began to affect every aspect of my life. My family was not middle-class, but neither were we amongst Jamaica's poorest. Though we lived in a tight space and could not afford to own a house, before the turmoil, we had all we needed and a little extra sometimes. But when I started noticing my mother struggling to provide meals for us and realized, after some time had passed, that it coincided with fewer visits from my dad, I began to pay even closer attention to the situation.

The situation became untenable when, one day, at my very prominent high school, the principal asked a few students to stay back in the hall after devotion. The batch that stayed behind was representative of the social mix in Jamaica – the rich, middle-class and the trying poor; together, we all wondered what we had done to warrant such a forum.

"What did we do wrong?" one girl whispered.

"I'm not sure," I said. "But we'll find out."

We were all nervous.

The principal was wearing her perennial smile, but this morning her smile did not reach her eyes as was often the case when we messed up. Then, in the quietness of the hall where more than a handful of girls were gathered, Miss Reader got right to the point while remaining on the podium.

"Girls, your school fees are outstanding. I have sent letters to your parents not once or twice but repeatedly to address this matter." She continued,

"We need to collect these fees . . . and, there will be 'dire consequences' if they remain outstanding."

She stared down at each of us standing before her for at least 30 seconds, not leaving anyone out of her probing gaze. Her thin lips remained turned up at the corners, but there was only the message in her eyes.

Then she said,

"You are dismissed. Please take the letters home to your parents or guardians when you each receive them this afternoon."

For me, this was an extremely embarrassing way to find out that I owed the school money. I knew things were tough at home, but were all the families represented in the room that morning now broke? I decided to ask my mom about this perilous matter affecting my school life.

"Mommy, how come I haven't been seeing Daddy these days when things are so hard?" I asked, as I handed her what seemed like the umpteenth letter from the school in recent weeks. "I found out this morning that my school fees not paid yet and I can never get the materials I need to do my school projects."

"Things are hard all over the country," my mother replied. "Did yuh write and tell your father what is happening?"

"No-o," I answered slowly, while turning the thought over in my mind. My father and I had a close relationship. Whenever he visited, he would sit on the verandah, and chitchat with me.

"San," my father would say, especially when I was in primary school, "Bring your books and show me all those A's."

He would go through my schoolbooks and ask numerous questions on topics I had already covered. He would be pleased with my work; I was a very good student, always at the top of my class at Half-Way-Tree Primary School. In high school, my work was also above average, at least up until then.

My father did not do this evaluation weekly, but this practice made him my hero. He was the person I wanted to please most and the person who made me know he had great expectations of me. Dad expected a daughter who would excel at school and 'speak properly' – that is, speak English and not the patois spoken by most Jamaicans. Dad himself was well spoken.

My letters to my father between these visits had always provided him with glowing reports on my performance in school, and sometimes other general matters. When I was nine years old, for example, I pierced my earlobes all by myself, inserting hairpins as a way of preventing them from resealing. I then wrote to my father and requested gold earrings. When my mom came home from work that evening and saw my new body piercings, I got a scolding for being too "own way". But, she rectified the problem by replacing my dangling makeshift jewellery with assumedly more hygienic temporary earrings, made from her thread collection.

The response I sought from my dad came within a couple of weeks. A crisp $5 bill was sandwiched in the fold of his handwritten letter to me. The sole purpose of the money was to purchase some real jewellery. But this current cash flow problem was going to be an entirely new topic to broach with him. With this thought, I proceeded to write a very open and honest letter to my dad about what was happening with us at home and with me at school.

This letter was different. It was not about my accomplishments, but rather about our daily struggles to maintain the life we knew and my personal fears and insecurities about not being able to afford to go to school. Dad had never heard anything like that from me before, but I expected his reassuring comfort in response.

It was late one night when my father arrived at our house. This was some weeks after I had sent him my letter. I deduced that he must have received the letter and decided to come in person to allay my concerns. I was getting ready for bed and wearing my pink nightdress when I heard my father's voice calling,

"Hello . . . goodnight!"

Elated at hearing his voice, I ran on to the verandah to greet him. I had missed him so badly over the last many long months!

"Hello Daddy!" My eyes lit up as I flung my arms around my father's neck, overcome with relief and happiness to see him.

His body was rigid.

I could hardly have anticipated his response.

My father pushed me away, using both hands! I stumbled backwards from the impact of his attack. I barely found my footing as my father began his scathing rebuke of me.

I did not know this man.

"Do you know what this girl did?" he bellowed. He seemed to be addressing some unseen judge, but I think he spoke indirectly to my mother who, upon hearing the commotion, was just coming out from our all-in-one living and dining room to the verandah. After all, she was responsible for me and by default, my iniquity.

"Wordsworth, what is going on?" she asked.

This was another first – because, I must tell you, I had never ever seen my parents interact with each other during my father's previous visits. All they ever did was exchange pleasantries.

There was one more alarming first. My father dropped his polished speech, seemingly to drive home the gravity of my misconduct.

"Yuh have any idea what she write in a letter to me? That it is because of me why yuh all starving!"

Mom did not respond to this statement. I just saw her swallow to fill the silence.

I began to tremble. For a moment, I could barely breathe. When he said it, it sounded so awful! I remembered being a little graphic in my letter, and maybe I had exaggerated a bit by using the word "starve", but I did not say it was his fault. I would not have accused my dad of such a thing; I worshipped him too much.

My father's face appeared as I had never seen it before. Disapproval contorted his features. In a split second, I knew that I had gone too far. How dare me, little more than a child, bring such adult matters out into the open.

My dad went into a tirade about the things that were happening in the country and how they had affected, no, "ruined his business".

"People are fleeing Jamaica, leaving their businesses behind and selling their large homes below value because of the course the politics has taken." He continued his lecture,

"Every day I am working harder than ever and not making any money. I can't even take advantage of the opportunity to buy any of the houses people are literally giving away on sale!"

I had been hearing snippets about these issues on the evening news, but it was all too clinical for me coming from my father. I felt like an idiot standing in front of him. In my moment of disgrace, Mom came to my rescue by ordering me to my room.

I rushed into the house and into my bed, whimpering. My father had never made me cry before this night. I could not keep up with wiping the heavy flow of scalding tears spilling from my eyes; the volume a testimony of how much things were about to change in my life.

My father never came back to see us after that night.

This change was enough evidence that I was not in a bad dream with him cursing me. And he never gave me any money or support thereafter. I never wrote to him ever again – out of both humiliation and defiance. My mom never acknowledged any of what transpired that night on our verandah. She had never spoken ill of my father before, and even when he publicly humiliated me, she said nothing. I cannot say why she never came to my defence – perhaps she just could not find the right words.

That was how my new life officially started in 1978.

At first, I tried to forget that horrible night my dad reprimanded me – no, rebuffed me openly because I dared to speak up about a matter affecting my wellbeing. For as long as I could, I clung to the memory of my earlier life, full of his love. Then, my life was almost perfect. I was secure – with a doting father, an ever-present mother, a great circle of family, friends, my own youthful achievements and hope. But trying to relive my previous life did not help me too much post age 14. After my father shut me down, I no longer felt I had license to speak for myself about the issues affecting me. Worse, I had to face the harsh reality that the father who I so idolized had abandoned me.

With this, I had become a full-fledged 'have-not', as my mom had by then lost her day job. While I did not fully understand the context of the changes in my country, I fully understood the changes my family was experiencing.

Just before I went to high school, Mom had left her job in downtown Kingston to go and work with Carmelita in a new distribution business she and her husband had set up. But, when things got rough, Carmelita decided to close her business, pack up and leave Jamaica. Mom said she was not surprised that Carmelita made the decision to go as so many Jamaicans were migrating.

Mom said Carmelita told her,

"Lyn, I didn't think I would ever leave Jamaica . . . I love Jamaica, but it seems like Jamaica no longer loves me."

"If yuh have to go, yuh have to go, Carmelita. I just wish I knew what going to happen to me and the children . . ." was my mother's reply.

And so I kissed my best friend Camellia and her family goodbye. On Manley's advice, they boarded one of the "five daily flights from Jamaica to Miami" and migrated to the US – Land of Opportunity. They left to escape the uncertainty of the social and political *ants nest* that Jamaica had become. But Mom had nowhere to run. She was already over 50 years old. It was too late for her to find work in a sluggish economy with a skyrocketing unemployment rate.

Thank God she had her sewing.

Before the changes brought on by the floundering economy, my mother sacrificed a great deal to ensure I had everything I needed for school. She knew the importance of a good education. Now the political strife and the lack of money were threatening to take away hope of a better life.

The changes came down on me in a deluge. Now life was about figuring out day-by-day who the new me was. I had to get used to the fact that some of the things I had taken for granted had become luxuries. The expectation of receiving lunch money daily, plus a sandwich to take to school, was no longer realistic. Having separate pairs of shoes for school and church was now unaffordable.

Imagine the fate of the black patent penny loafers with the block heels that my grand-aunt, Ivy, had sent me from England. They were my church shoes when I first got them. I had to turn to them to stay in the education lane. They did not fit the uniform code and my form teacher told me not to wear them back to school, but I told her that they were all I had. She understood.

Next were the meal changes at home. I was never a big fan of meat dishes. I preferred chicken, but now I had to settle for its more affordable bony sections like the back strip, prepared in a variety of styles, but thankfully pleasing to the palate. We ate a lot of this part of the chicken – curried or stewed – served with fluffy white rice or dumplings and bananas, Monday to Wednesday. On Thursdays, we had a one-pot meal of seasoned rice with ackee and traces of saltfish.

On Fridays, there was no cooking in most Jamaican households, so we picked around on bun and cheese or other snacks. Then on Saturdays, it could be either chicken back or chicken foot for soup. We never complained because we knew that on Sundays, Mom would do her best to cook the traditional dish consisting of an entire chicken, pot roasted, with rice and peas, vegetables and sometimes potato salad.

However, my hours away from home were tricky. I had grown very self-conscious. I agonized each day about how best to disguise my steady social decline. Looking into my school population, one would have seen the cross section of races and ethnic groups, with their corresponding variations in shades of complexion, nicely intermingling. Some of my peers were from the known wealthy Jamaican families, others from the merchant class and from families of leading politicians. Another set was from families of very accomplished professionals; and that left us, from the working class, hoping to move up to a better life.

There was seldom any display of snobbery from the privileged students, but those of us not so well endowed materially stood out easily – it was like being caught under a searchlight while breaking a curfew.

I did not pay tuition because of the government's free education policy. But the truth was that my family could no longer even afford the cost of the auxiliary fees for me to access free secondary education. I did not want the sirens going off regarding my domestic conundrum.

Worrying about being able to stay in school was enough pressure for a teenager, but the added dimension of my father holding me in contempt indefinitely, led to my feelings of shame and worthlessness. I felt that my lack of worth was obvious, as if it were pinned on my collar like a badge for all to see. This occupied my thoughts daily and my grades deteriorated. I lost interest in school. I tried desperately to adapt to living in my new and unwelcome world. My only solace was in my poetry writing.

Many evenings, I took my habitual journey into my fantasy world where I would write about feeling lonely and rejected. Writing about my longings and my ordeal was the only remedy for the rough passage from sheltered to lost. I turned to the rhythm of words to salve my soul. The words poured onto paper as I sat on my once sacred verandah, surrounded by my schoolbooks, for which I had lost my appetite. I created my own world as I felt that no one could understand my anxieties or would even care to know of them.

Just a few years before these challenging times, I had become a 'born again' Christian. First when I wrote, it was always about God and His merciful salvation. Now I struggled to find strength in the joy of the Lord. I felt that God too had abandoned me, even though deep down I knew He was somewhere up there looking down on me. So, I prayed unceasingly for forgiveness from whichever sin I had committed to cause my life to plunge into such misery.

3

Staying Afloat

I ESCAPED MY GRIEF BY FALLING in love with a boy named Dave. Somehow, I expected that my first crush (not counting Everton from the 5th grade at primary school) would take me back to my happier days by expunging the hurt my father had caused me.

Dave was the cutest young man in our age group at church. Of course, to this day, he has no idea that he was the object of my romantic thoughts and my inspiration for writing a new genre of searing love poetry.

You may laugh now, but back then, it was not funny. It was just an immature adoration, but it temporarily subdued my pain. However, love is not always comforting, especially when unreciprocated. The problem was that Dave was not interested in chasing girls. He was focusing on his Christianity and his schoolbooks. He was a bit boring by today's standards for boyfriends, but none of that served to deter my interest in him and I constantly craved his attention. It was not easy keeping my new secret love close to my heart, but it was a necessary distraction from my unhappiness as it had become very hard to hide the pain of losing my father's love from those who knew me.

Against this ambivalence, my crush on Dave intensified. Being in love was my daily focus, even though as a newly converted Christian I was supposed to have been "wrapped-up, tied-up and tangled-up with Jesus". Jesus was supposed to be "my all-in-all". However, rather than singing lustily from my *Hymns of Light and Love* each Sunday morning, I was allowing my compulsive habit of staring into the back of my imaginary boyfriend's head to consume me.

I tried everything to get Dave's attention without being direct, but nothing happened. The magic between us was only in my mind. I decided to write him a letter – despite my recent blunder with this mode of communication. I thought the timing was perfect. The idea came at the point when I noticed Dave was not attending young people's meetings and had also missed the Breaking of Bread service two Sundays in a row.

"You are missing out on rich worship," I said.

"You are such a smart young man and all the young people here admire you." I went on, "Please don't stay away from church for too long; we miss you and want you to come and fellowship with us weekly."

It was short and to the point. I hoped it would serve my selfish purpose of seeing my 'boyfriend' soon.

Dave did not show up at church the next Sunday either, but I was determined to deliver this letter. I sat strategically in the bench behind his family and bravely leaned forward and handed Dave's dad the letter during the offering collection.

"Good morning Brother Phillips," I whispered, while handing him the letter. "I notice Dave isn't here this morning. Can you kindly give him this note for me?"

"Certainly." Dave's dad replied and nodded courteously.

Foolish idea.

In what looked like slow motion, I saw Dave's dad tear open the envelope that was clearly addressed to his son, unfold the letter, whip his eyeglasses out of the breast pocket of his bush jacket and proceed to read its contents.

I wanted to crawl under the church bench.

Then I remembered that my marginal wisdom had prevented me from declaring any sort of love in the letter, thanks be unto God. I remained seated but felt very exposed. Neither father nor son mentioned the letter when they next turned up at church. It was as if it never happened and for that I was grateful.

That marked the end of my obsession with writing unsolicited letters. I must confess too that my one-sided love affair was getting a bit irritating, as Dave continued to be unresponsive to my pheromones. Dave may have been an unwilling boyfriend, but being in love was in vogue, and I was not in a hurry to give up my crush. After all, one of my friends at school, Melody, was also in love and she was happy.

But Melody's love affair was the reverse of what I was

experiencing. Hers was like a fairy tale. It was easy to believe she had found love, as she was one of the most friendly and popular girls in my form. Melody was also quite a fashionista – popping her collar to add some pizzazz to what would have been our rather plain uniform. She had met her boyfriend on an educational trip to Mexico, arranged by the interschool Spanish fraternity. Melody's new beau was from one of the local boys' schools that had participated in the trip.

Of course, I was unable to go on the trip. I had neither the passport nor the airfare. However, a year later, I took my first flight out of the island. I went home with my friend, Mitzy, who was from Grand Cayman and attending school in Jamaica. She had invited me to visit her home for the Easter holidays and Mom trumped up all the money she could find to make this trip happen. My mother had never met Mitzy's parents, but had heard enough from me about how near-perfect Mitzy and her family were, to send me off, on a plane, for a week, to a place she herself had only heard about.

Grand Cayman was like a nice little beach town when I first visited the island. On arrival, it felt like I had landed on the beach, its salty fragrance greeting us on the tarmac as we alighted from the plane. They were not big on fences in Cayman and everywhere seemed open and accessible. Back then, it was almost free of high-rise buildings, and sparsely populated. Today it looks quite different. I went into the town with my friend's family and got some questioning stares from the locals. I heard one woman ask Mitzy if I was an 'Onion'.

"Onion?" I asked my friend. "Why would she call me that?"

"Oh," Mitzy paused, "*Higglers* come here regularly to shop for goods that are scarce in Jamaica." She was being her diplomatic self.

"Onion is one of the items at the top of their list, that's how they got that name."

This was of course during the times of restricted imports of both necessary and luxury items. The encounter, however, would not blemish my memories of a very gratifying and pleasant holiday in Cayman that Easter. Jamaica and Cayman have a special connection that predates hard times. I went to Seven Mile Beach, went on bicycle rides, ate turtle meat and made French toast with my friend and her peppy little sister, while her parents were busy managing their business. So, even though I did not find love in a foreign land, as Melody had, Cayman gave me other enriching experiences.

I cannot remember the fine details of Melody's love story set in Mexico City, but each day during our lunch break, we would all be captivated by the latest episode of her exciting love life.

"Peter is so attentive and understanding," she would say blushingly. "I honestly didn't think I would meet anyone like him.

"Peter invited me to go to dinner with his family." And

"… Peter … etc., etc."; always something thoughtful that Peter had done for her. She made him sound very impressive and when I met him, he was as nice as she made him out to be.

I, on the other hand, never spoke about Dave. What would I say? I thought it best to allow my love for Dave to remain in the private chambers of my heart. Writing love poetry continued to be my sole outlet and secret vice.

Slowly, my crush on Dave began to fade. Reality had caught up with me and I realized that my puerile love interest and imaginings were no longer capable of offering relief from my sorrows. It had, however, equipped me with a penchant for stringing words together in a rhythmic way that brought perspective to my otherwise meaningless life. Maybe I was more in love with my written words than with Dave. I gave up my crush on Dave but went on stumbling through my life, for it seemed like at my age, I had known too much loss and needed to somehow block it out.

During those immediate years after my father disappeared from our lives, my mother worked hard to make ends meet. One of her devices was to take in a boarder or two despite the limited space we had. And whether the boarding fees were forthcoming or not, Mommy, as everyone called her, always took care of her boarders.

She combined the boarding with her long-time sewing

hustle, broadening her clientele beyond friends and family members. Now Mom was sewing for anyone friends had recommended, so that she could pay the bills, feed us and ensure that we had the bus fare to get to school. On some days the lunch money was not enough or non-existent, but Mom would 'rustle up' sandwiches seemingly from thin air.

Oftentimes my mom's clients did not turn up for their clothes as scheduled. For weeks, sometimes months, she would get no payment for her efforts. There was always a neat pile of uncollected clothes on an old coffee table in one corner of her bedroom, but she kept on sewing – cutting, stitching and humming away as if this were her sacrament in life.

She seemed to be in control of the situation. I never saw her shed a tear and never heard her complain about how hard things were, but I certainly felt it. What she silently taught me then was that you should persevere and keep doing your best to stay on top of circumstances, no matter what they are or how they come your way. It took me a while before I fully appreciated this lesson.

Even through the resilience my mom exhibited, I perceived that there was an underlying anguish about her. Yet, she did everything to protect us from it – she never lashed out at us in frustration as some other parents in similar circumstances might have done. I believe Mom's private distress must have gone into her work, because in those days that was all she ever did. She no longer had Brenda to assist her with the sewing and cooking. After Brenda left and while she still had a nine-to-five job, Mom had someone come in to assist her with the washing, ironing and cleaning one day per week. This allowed her more time for her sewing. Now she was doing it all on her own, though we pitched in with our chores.

We woke up with Mom in the kitchen, fixing breakfast and sometimes lunch for us to take to school, and went to bed with her at her Singer sewing machine – its whirring sound like a lullaby sending us off to sleep and assuring us that everything would be OK the next morning. I never really saw my mom in bed until many years later when a stroke disabled her and, even then, she tried to run her household while struggling to sit up on the side of her bed or from her wheelchair.

I appreciated all that my mother did to provide for us, but what seemed like her over-dedication to work left me lonely. Maybe we grew apart during that time, because I had become a little rebellious after the near-fracas with my dad – an unreachable teenager arguing with my mother instead of heeding her instructions without question.

There was that occasion when she agreed that I could go to my school's bar-b-que after I begged her for an entire week to allow me to go. She relented. I went. I did not return home that night, but I had a good explanation, which Mom did not accept.

"Good morning Mommy," I greeted her early the next day.

"Good morning? Where yuh were, Sanaa? Yuh know I

was up all night, just short of calling the police to report yuh missing?" she snapped.

"What was our agreement, young lady, eeh?"

"That I should get a ride with Melody but. . ." Mom cut me off right there.

"Sanaa! I don't want to hear it! This is not what I expect from yuh!" Just know that yuh won't be going anywhere but school and church for a long time."

She wheeled away, leaving me with my explanation unaired.

We had no home phone and Melody had left me at the bar-b-que, so I got a ride with another schoolmate. I told her I could not go home at that late hour as my mother had expected me earlier, and so I spent the night at her home. When her dad had come to pick her up and she had given him the silly explanation that I had given her, he looked appalled – as if he thought my Mom would have brutalized me for coming in late.

Some say teenagers do crazy things to get their parents' attention and perhaps that was the real explanation for my uncharacteristic behaviour. My daily life was like treading water in rough seas. I was not feeling the closeness I had with my mother and that did not help my situation. The conversations Mom and I used to have when I would sit at the foot of her bed, while she pumped away at the sewing machine, had ceased. The games we used to play at nights before turning in had long lost their appeal. The stories I used to hear from her about her youthful escapades with

Linda, her half-sister and her good times with my dad, I already knew line-by-line.

My mom had grown up with her mother but had spent some time living with her father as well. Her parents lived on opposite sides of Kingston. Her father's house was in Franklin Town on the eastern side of Kingston, and this was where she had had her good times. Her mother's house was miles away in Shortwood on the northern side of Kingston, but the times spent there were less fun-filled – mainly because she had lived alone with her mother.

My favourite story, which I begged my mom to tell me over and over again, was of her, her sister Linda and their cousin Tina diverting from Elletson Primary School to go to sports day at the Bellevue Hospital for mentally challenged persons. Bellevue was in Rockfort, just a little distance from Franklin Town. This trip was charged with excitement. They had not sought their father's permission to go, because he was a very strict man.

It was thrilling for them to see the inmates running in races against each other, but more hilarious were the competitors' impromptu sideshows before they reached the finish line. This excitement, coupled with the dread of the adults at home finding out about their unauthorized spree, was exhilarating for Mom and company.

They had a great time, but their day did not end well.

My grandfather used to keep a few shillings and other coins in a little nook behind the latticework above the living room door. It had occurred to them in planning their trip that they should borrow one of these shillings for this big event.

"How else we going to fund our treats?"

"Dada couldn't possibly miss one shilling out of so many," they reasoned.

This faulty reasoning was their undoing. When they got home just before dusk, they saw Grandpa in his merino and underpants sitting on the patio in his rocking chair, cane in hand. They shuffled amongst themselves, none wanting to be the first to enter the yard or patio. Eventually they filed in, Mom, being the bravest, leading the way to their unavoidable cross-examination and punishment. After a few questions to them regarding their whereabouts and, to their horror, his missing shilling, to which they could give only stuttering answers, Grandpa administered some corporal punishment and sent them to bed without supper. That was their first and last visit to Bellevue Sports Day.

However, cheerful storytelling times like these had passed with my previous life. All these tales dried up when our lives changed so dramatically.

Now, Mom and I each lived in our own separate worlds – silence and pain. I felt alone, even though our home always seemed over-occupied.

Before Brenda moved back to the country, her sisters would visit Kingston and, naturally, they stayed at our house. After moving from Hagley Park, our new house was really a one-bedroom flat, but Mom used the space creatively. Our immediate family of three shared the large bedroom. Mom used a screen to divide the room and to give Gary the feeling of having his own space; there he had his small bed and chest of drawers. Mom and I shared her double bed and bureau in the larger space. We all shared a wardrobe which was at the right, upon entering the room. This served to block direct entry to Gary's corner from the living room. Mom packed our four-seat dining table and refrigerator into the living room along with the sofa, a bookshelf and a small coffee table. Her sewing machine found itself in a little passage between the living room and the room adjoining the kitchenette, originally intended as the dining room. The dining room became a second bedroom for Brenda and her family whenever they visited.

After Brenda left, her sisters still came by and sometimes stayed for extended periods – presumably looking for work in 'town'. It seemed like there was always at least one of the three visiting, but sometimes two. My mom never seemed to notice because she had enough love to go around. I got lost somewhere in the babble and flurry the sisters' presence usually created. But their visits were sure to break the doldrums to which I had become accustomed.

Admittedly, it was always exciting when they arrived, as Brenda sent us all the things she knew we loved from the country – mangoes, oranges, sugar cane, roasted cashew nuts and chocolate balls for making that delicious hot beverage. And, of course, they were expected to bring some of those prized herbs that everyone believed to be curative. Mom would be delighted to get some cerasee – she would make tea from it and sip it continuously to help regulate her 'sugar' (diabetes). From time to time, she would crush the cerasee bush and mix it with bay rum – or carbolic soap if she was out of bay rum – and then use the mixture like a body scrub on us, the younger members of the household, if she felt that we were not "bathin' good".

However, I was almost panic-stricken when I realized that Brenda's eldest sister Jeannie, along with her young daughter, were not on a brief or even extended visit. They were going to be living with us! Apparently, the lack of space was not a concern for Jeannie – maybe because she had grown up in a large family.

Jeannie did not create any ripples in our household. You hardly knew she was there, even though she stayed for a long while – over a year – before moving out on her own. Then, when Jeannie later got a job in the Cayman Islands, she left her daughter with us. Jeannie's daughter was, in fact, my mom's first official boarder to help her keep her household afloat in the tough economic times.

Most often I would tune out the many people in my home. I felt I had no connection with this earthly world. I lived somewhere between the world I created from flowery words and the real world. This was how I carved out a space for myself.

I'm not sure if there is yet a single word that accurately captures what really happens to a young adolescent girl after she experiences abandonment and rejection, especially by a father she once revered. Perhaps not, but she is required to cope one way or another. My poetry was not enough of an escape for my misery and I did not know how to go on living in my vague world.

I had stopped eating. Whenever I ate because Mom insisted, I overdid it – only to expel the food in disgust at myself just minutes after feasting. I became thin and I lost interest in day-to-day activities.

One of my church elders intervened.

It was a Friday night, after Young People's Meeting. Typically, he would drop his daughter at the church and then wait around in the church office or church yard until the service ended, to take her home. Sometimes you would see him standing at the side of the church hall, peeking in at us through a window as if checking our devoutness.

He must have been observing me closely that night and apparently, lately.

"Sanaa," Elder Grange accosted me.

"I notice you've become withdrawn – you're not participating in any of the church activities these days."

He was right. There I was, just sitting by myself at one end of a bench reading a bible passage when all the other young folks were laughing and chatting after the meeting. Once upon a time, I would have been in the centre of the conversations.

"What's wrong?"

"I'm fine, Sir."

"Are you sure nothing is wrong? Tell me the truth."

"I guess I miss Brenda Sir; she went back to the country."

"Oh . . . OK; yes, I knew you were very close to her . . ."

Of course he knew who Brenda was, but he also knew she had gone for quite some time now. Nevertheless, I used that situation to avoid telling him any details, kind as he was. Then he said,

"I will pray for you . . ."

I nodded, acknowledging his kindness. God knows I needed the prayers.

At school, my form teacher sent me to see the guidance counsellor when my schoolwork fell off. I found a clever way to get out of that too. In the first (and only) session, I heard myself telling the counsellor that my mom was also a counsellor. End of session; no further questions asked.

I did not want to talk to anyone about my issues – no one would understand, and I was afraid that if I interacted with others they would see my pain. I chose to be alone and to keep my business to myself – jotting down my feelings in my little homemade journal when shame, guilt or loneliness washed over me. Even if I felt sorry for myself, I did not want anyone's pity.

To many persons, I must have seemed aloof, but I was just hurting.

4

Going On

A LITTLE MORE THAN A YEAR after the unfortunate incident with my father, we moved house again. This change helped me push the memory of my father's unforeseen rage further back in my mind. In fact, that is when I first buried him. I simply decided that since I did not have a father in my life it would be wise to think of him as dead, or better, not to think of him at all.

We settled nicely into the new and spacious, much airier house, with a big, fruited yard, in a close-knit neighbourhood further up Shortwood Road. It felt like a fresh start for our family – as if we could finally leave all the mishaps behind. Where we lived before, I would stay behind my gate and watch the neighbourhood kids skipping freely in the narrow avenue. I had no such freedom. Happily, that life was behind me.

Now I could venture beyond my gate and visit with some of the young people in my new neighbourhood who, no doubt, shared my values and aspirations. This was new to me. After Camellia and her family migrated, I barely had any friends outside of school or church, except my godsister, Prudence, who soon migrated to America. So these changes were good, and I was eager to get on with my life. But, somehow, even with all the new friends and neighbours, I still felt vanquished; I still had to wrestle with feelings of wretchedness. I felt as if I were in a cylinder with no bottom – no father to protect me, to prevent me from falling. No father to validate my efforts.

My new neighbours had never seen my father and they knew nothing about him. They may have thought he was somewhere out there, perhaps overseas and I pretended as if nothing was amiss; female-headed households were common across Jamaica.

In my early life, I had felt that I was different from the children I met who did not have a father or even know their father. After all, I had a father who cared for me, even though he did not live with me. How ironic; I too was now fatherless. These were the thoughts in my subconscious that constantly chipped away at my sense of self.

Financially, things were not easing up for us at home just yet. Moving to the new house was divine intervention. The owners were our church brethren and they had given us a good deal on the rent because they were migrating. Notwithstanding, all the bills were now higher than before.

Mom amped up the boarding. Some came for months, others for years.

The interesting personalities that came to live with us broke the gloom we previously knew. One such personality was Gregory, or Greg as we called him. Greg was a sort of indirect cousin of ours. Kay, my mom's niece living in New York, was adopting him and wanted him to stay with us until she could finalize his adoption papers.

Two years before, when we lived at the previous house, my mother's youngest sister in New York had sent her sick, six-year-old son to stay with us for six months. It seems the news spread to family abroad that they could send relatives to Lynette in Jamaica for a 'quick fix'. If they had a sick child, Lyn would get him or her on the road to recovery. If they had a slow child, Lyn would help him or her to catch up on schoolwork. If they had a problem child, Lyn would straighten him or her out.

This is how Greg came to us and we all welcomed him. My cousin wanted Greg to get away from his volatile inner-city community and felt he could get some 'refinement' while living with my mom. Greg was about eight years old; he wanted to become an athlete and could run fast despite his severe case of knock-knees. He could not read well and had no interest in learning. Mom set out to work on him with a home-designed reading programme, starting from the basics using the ABC Alphabet Book. She had her hands full.

Very quickly, we found out that Greg had sticky fingers. The very first day he arrived, Greg swiped two sticks of Wrigley's chewing gum from my dresser and 'found' a two-dollar bill that just happened to be "on the floor" in the bedroom he was sharing with Gary and Tony. Of course, his sins came to light soon enough and Gary dealt with him accordingly. Greg never stole from us again, but my mother would get various reports from school (via Jeannie's daughter who was in the same grade) about his many transgressions.

There was the time, for example, when he came home from school bruised and covered in milk powder. The entire school had turned on him because he tried to swindle another child of his milk-powder allowance, which was provided to every primary school child seasonally, courtesy of the government. You may say Greg got his due. Despite my mom's best efforts at refining him – each morning religiously drumming into him as he went through the door "Show mi yuh company an' I'll tell yuh who yuh are" – when Greg migrated to the US, he got mixed up with the wrong crowd. He got in trouble with the law and the US authorities eventually deported him to Jamaica.

A year later, the same cousin who had entrusted us with Greg, sent us her 80-something-year-old grandmother-in-law, Gramps. Gramps pretended to be independent. She refused to stay in bed and ambled around the house, moving slowly, her back stooped from many years of dependence on a walking stick. Despite her age and physical challenges, she had a strong voice and a good memory. Her piercing eyes missed nothing; and she would often accuse Tony of taking her things if she saw him just carrying a bag out of the house. Gramps was a very irreverent old lady and when she was in a good mood, she would leave us in stitches from the jokes she told us, some quite raunchy, about her romantic experiences as a young woman.

"When I was young, I had a suitor that my father wanted me to marry. But I didn't like him none at all. Yuh know how I got away from him?" Gramps asked. We were all silent, waiting.

"Him went to teach in the country. When my father didn't see him for a few weeks he asked me what happened to him and why he wasn't visiting us.

'I hear he's in prison . . . for stealing a pig Papa.'

'What? I don't want any pig tief in this family. Yuh just mek sure him don't come back here!' "

Gramps' belly jiggled with laughter as she recalled her disingenuousness.

It was also an event in our household when Gramps got aggravated. She would grumble for days at a time – stopping only when her head of thinning silver hair hit the pillow after she had had her supper, but resuming her rant at the break of day. Her grouse was that we were "working obeah (witchcraft)" on her.

One day my mom decided to record Gramps' grumblings on tape, and later played it back to her when she was in less of a temper. Gramps swore it was not her voice on the tape and that the recording was merely evidence of the high science to which she had alluded. Unfazed, Gramps wagged her index finger at my mom and ominously threw out her favourite saying:

"The truth going to swim in here like how oil swim

'pon water."

You could not win with Gramps. Mom put up with her crankiness for about three years until her family moved her to a nursing home.

My favourite among those passing through our home was Cousin Kay's daughter and Gramps' great-granddaughter, Norah. The purpose of her visit was twofold – first, to spend time with her great granny and second, to give Kay a break after she had gone through a tough separation from her husband, Norah's dad.

On the very first day she arrived at our house, Norah declared that she was a tomboy. She certainly did not have a frail structure and spent a lot of time climbing the trees in the yard and play-fighting with Tony and Greg. Underneath all that, the person I saw was a vivacious young girl who embraced life and all her newfound relatives in Jamaica. She was also a soft-hearted soul trying to disguise her true nature by displaying a tough exterior.

After that first summer with us, Kay decided that Norah would benefit from the education system in Jamaica and, for the next eight years, she sent her daughter to a boarding school on the south coast of Jamaica. Norah was disappointed at not living with us and not attending school in Kingston, but her years at boarding school served to mature her. When she completed her A' level examinations she returned to New York to attend college. I saw Norah on my first visit to New York and was relieved to see that she was still her vivacious self.

It was after we moved that I discovered that I was not just a dreamer – one who wanted a perfect family and home – but that I was also resourceful. My survival instincts kicked in one day when one of my friends brought some chocolate fudge to school. I remembered that I had seen a recipe for something similar in a book at home titled *Things to Make and Do*. I went home that afternoon, looked up the recipe and made some fudge. It was the same fudge.

The next day I took some of my freshly made fudge to school and my friends loved it.

"Yuh can bring some more tomorrow?"

"No problem," my enterprising self said. "But I will need a small fee to cover the cost of the ingredients."

Would they be willing to pay? Of course they would pay! After all, the canteen offered no such treats; the nearest offer was Ping Pong (peanuts thinly coated in chocolate) and that was always in limited supply. It was a grand opportunity to ease the burden off my mom by selling this fudge so that she did not have to provide everything for me.

Every evening after that, I made chocolate fudge. It cut into my time studying Shakespeare and West Indian history with Isaac Dookham, but it had to be done. For more than a year, I discreetly distributed the product to my schoolmates for a small fee to generate my lunch money and bus fare for school. The income from my fudge sales would eventually help with offsetting my graduation fees. I saved fervently for this event, as I felt very encouraged to do so after Mom astonishingly came up with all my grade 11 exam fees, just in time to meet the deadline for payment!

I had inherited a can-do spirit from my mom and St Andrew High School for Girls fostered it. It was our school spirit. Forget about circumstances; if you wanted to express your talent or strength – be it in academics, sports, or the arts – you could find your space there. This accommodation promoted tolerance for differences and supported our strengths. I doubt that anyone knew that I needed to be enterprising, but because I did it with enthusiasm, my schoolmates supported me as I streamlined my newly found business into a profitable operation.

My upbeat salesmanship however, was just a veneer for hiding my lingering sadness. With my stoic mom, you knew that the last thing she expected was moping. For her, such display of emotions indicated weakness and so I pulled myself together and tried to appreciate the changes in my condition. Things were getting better, and I had even regained interest in my classes.

One day, I decided to visit a friend, Natalie, who lived just a few avenues away from me. It was during the mid-term break and we had agreed to study together to prepare for our upcoming exams. Natalie was from a different type of family than mine. Her home was somewhat unstructured as her mother worked out of town and was away most of the time. Though her dad lived with them, he was hardly ever there; they were, basically, in charge of themselves – no interfering parents. Natalie had an older brother, Cliff, who seemed a little sneaky. I never spoke much with

Cliff, but clearly, as I was to discover on that study day, he must have had his eyes set on me for some time.

After I arrived at her house, Natalie and her sister decided to go on an errand to the nearby grocery store to get something they needed for that day's dinner. As soon as they left, Cliff seemed to appear out of nowhere. I was sitting in the sofa in their dimly lit living room, reading an old copy of a Mills & Boon novel I had found on a side table next to the sofa, when I felt someone hovering over me.

"What yuh reading?" Cliff asked.

I did not really feel like talking.

"Yuh can't see?" I retorted in my most sarcastic tone without looking up, hoping to dismiss him. But he remained there until I finally said,

"It's a Mills & Boon."

"You girls an' yuh Mills & Boon," Cliff shot back. "Yuh need the real stuff."

That got my attention. Cliff's menacing tone sent a chill through my body, a signal for me to flee but I was immobilized as he moved in closer to me. For the first time, I looked Cliff square in the face, noticing his close-set eyes. His jaws were clenched, and his arms folded. His aggressive invasion of my personal space confirmed to me that this was not going to be a friendly situation. I moved to stand up, but Cliff moved faster. Falling to his knees, he pinned me down on the sofa. I did not know what to do. I mustered the strength to plead in a weak, jagged voice.

"No Cliff, please, yuh can't do this; I don't want to do this!"

Cliff ignored me, pressing on with his sleazy intentions. I struggled, and Cliff paused for a while, warning me in his still menacing voice not to make any noise.

"Just easy!"

My body went dead but my mind was screaming. I lay there stiffly coiled, while Cliff attempted to violate my innocence – stopping short of fully assaulting me at the squeak of the front gate. His sisters had returned. This threw him off guard. In a flash, I commanded my motor skills and with trembling legs, I headed for the back door of his house. I barely escaped the embarrassment of facing my friend, looking dishevelled and with teary eyes.

What if Cliff's sisters had not returned when they did? I did not want to believe that he would have gone any further.

I scrambled home, my head spinning in disbelieve of what had happened. I took a long shower as I tried to remove the blemish of Cliff's touch from my body. I sobbed silently, hoping my mom would not suspect anything peculiar about my actions at that time of the day. She did not, and I was relieved that I did not have to tell her about Cliff's crude sexual advance. She certainly would have done him harm . . . and we would all be living our own regrets.

I trembled for days after and tried to push Cliff's attack out of my mind. I felt ashamed and blamed myself for somehow unknowingly inviting his unwanted attention, for him humiliating and desecrating me with his roving hands and eyes. But this was not enough for Cliff. It seemed that his mission was to destroy me. I had to pass his backyard on the way to school and church. Whenever I passed him there – holding my head straight because I could not look him in the eye after that terrible incident – he would laugh and say,

"Grow up."

I felt so despondent about the whole matter that I decided to unburden myself by sharing my experience with a kind, older woman at my church. She was a returning resident and had taken to me as she had no children of her own. Talking about this calamity helped me to release some of the self-judgement and blame that I had assumed. Over time, I coped by just trying to block out the memory of what Cliff had done to me; just as I had done with my father. I never went back to visit my friend at home, and eventually, when they moved from the neighbourhood, it became easier for me to live with myself.

But Cliff's whispered slurs to "grow up" had stuck with me and I guess in some twisted way I agreed with him that I needed to grow up. I became determined to be more mature about life.

What exactly did that mean? I was turning 16, had all the physical attributes associated with becoming a young woman, but I was very inept regarding intimate relationships. Mom would never allow me to become involved with boys. Furthermore, as a Christian, thinking about sex was a no-no. In my church, our elders challenged us to remain chaste; free from even sexual thoughts, until marriage. This meant avoiding any romantic involvement until well after school, at least. This was my goal.

I was soon thrown into another situation that would move me along the maturity belt when I got a surprise sweet-sixteen birthday party. Everything that happened that night was indeed a surprise. My eldest brother, Errol, had planned this party. Errol – my mother's first child – is about 15 years my senior. He left Mom to live with his paternal grandmother just before I was born. When I was little, he would visit and spend some Sunday afternoons with us and then after a while, when he started working, he would come by from time-to-time in the evenings after work. I would describe Errol as easy-going and likeable. Everyone was happy to see him whenever he came by for a visit.

The day of the party, he and Gary had been shifting around the furniture in the living room to create a dance floor and I did not have any clue about what was happening. We had never had a party at home before. Later in the evening, I found out that it was all for me. I let loose and danced all night, enjoying myself as I had never known it was possible to do at home. It was also a sort of 'coming out' for me, for it was at my birthday party that Mark, this 'cool' guy from the neighbourhood, first noticed me. I knew that he liked me instantly because of how he gazed at me and commanded most of my dances. Before the end of the night, we had become friends. We had just finished dancing to Earth Wind and Fire's *Boogie Wonderland* when he sought to find out my romantic status.

"Sanaa, yuh didn't invite anyone special to yuh party?" he inquired.

"Anyone special like who yuh mean?" I was playing with him, knowing full well what he meant.

"I mean like a boyfriend," Mark chuckled.

"No sah! I don't have one of those!"

"How come a girl like you single? Yuh need someone to protect yuh; to take care of yuh." I giggled as Mark went on about how much he liked me and how cute I was.

Here was my opportunity to grow up, but I was still not confident enough to go down that road.

Mark was much older than I was. He was very dapper and quite an attractive young man. We kept running into each other after the party. Wow! What a warm feeling I got when Mark flirted with me – but, I was unsure of how to respond. I dreaded that I would embarrass myself. I felt the normal sexual urges that a teenager experiences due to hormonal changes, but I was afraid of getting close to Mark or any other young man because of the disturbing memory of the repulsive, uninvited intimacy that Cliff had foisted upon me.

Yet, I wanted to experience what my friends at school spoke about daily. For, no matter how pious you try to be, romance is always enticing.

Having combined and internalized all the juicy tales I heard at school about teenage love, with themes from the romance novels I used to devour, I worked hard to modify my closed demeanour into one that portrayed confidence. I decided it was time to be more engaging with the opposite sex. I bought Mark the latest number one selling R&B album and, sure enough, that got his attention. But Mark was slick. The truth is, not only was he dangerously older than I was, but he was already involved with someone in his age range. Though he found me quite intriguing (my words), it was just bad luck on my part that he was spoken for. He had no intention of going beyond flirting with me.

This brief interlude with Mark obviously was not really a relationship, just an acknowledgement of our appreciation for each other. But it led to greater self-awareness. I was finding out that becoming a young woman was far more complex than experiencing some reproductive changes. Having someone to relate to outside of my community triangle of home, school and church – all of which I had lost touch with – helped me to rejoin the real world and to reconnect with myself. Sharing with Mark reminded me that I did not have to be afraid of the opposite sex. The way Mark related to me was, surprisingly, platonic. Despite the flirting that started at my party, Mark and I had become real friends. If Mark had been a lesser man, he could have taken advantage of me in my immature and vulnerable state, but he did not exploit my misguided infatuation.

While assimilating the changes in my life, I kept a watchful eye on politics.

Out there in the real world, the much-anticipated 1980 elections had come and gone in one day, on October 30, almost instantly ending the tension and grimness that had permeated the air for the better part of two years. It was a landslide victory for the JLP. They won 51 of 60 seats contested.

Every day leading up to the election, there had been news of murder and bloodshed on the TV, on the radio and in the newspapers. These unprecedented atrocities were a result of the strong intolerance some people had for others who did not share their ideology.

The warfare rose to a deafening crescendo as it snuffed out lives each day, until just before Election Day. The murders totalled over 800 before that day – the highest ever up to that time. The country was almost on its last breath.

Some Jamaicans may have never personally witnessed any violence or experienced any other type of displacement during this period, but we were all battle fatigued. We had lived through the psychological horrors of the political power struggle.

So, when the election was over, everyone was relieved and expectant, waiting for things to return to normal.

Next school day, my friends and I gathered under the lignum vitae tree to have our lunch and discuss the topic of the day – the epic election.

"Oh Lord, I'm so glad this whole election thing is all

over," Mitzy said.

"I hope this new 'Deliverer' can really give us what him promise, now that he's in charge," I chimed.

"But before yuh talk about new Deliverer Sanaa, yuh really thought that Michael Manley would lose to Edward Phillip George Seaga?"

We all laughed out in unison as loudly as we could on the school compound. That was the way the new prime minister liked to refer to himself, by his full name, in third person.

"Well, new prime minister is promising us a more peaceful and prosperous nation," I said.

"I don't care who win, I just want change . . . a better life."

The opinionated Alice piped up,

"But Sanaa," she said, "Why yuh think Michael Manley really lost the election?"

We all went silent for a moment.

Michael Manley may have lost the election, but we did not feel it was our place to openly question anything about him or his politics after his defeat. I had read that Manley was a scholar. He was also well disposed to political leadership because of his family's history in politics.

When you saw Manley on the 7pm news almost every night, he was full of energy and interacting with all the people he encountered; and you knew why he was loved. His good looks and chiselled physique helped to make him very popular too. He relaxed the look-of-the-day for men in parliament by choosing to wear Kariba suits – a substitute for the traditional long-sleeved jackets worn with a shirt and a tie. That aside, it was Michael Manley's experience as a former trade unionist that put him out front in Jamaican politics. It made him sensitive to the plight of the working class, despite his privileged position in the Jamaican society as an almost-white man of means.

"Yuh know why . . . because some persons said he is communist, and that Jamaica would no longer be a free country if he should win," Alice answered her own question when no one responded.

"But we've discussed this already," I reminded my friend.

To be fair to Manley, what he had espoused was 'democratic socialism' – not communism. He had never proposed a dictatorship under a one-party state; rather, a government-run economy. Democratic socialism was not a euphemism for communism. But the name of the politics was of little importance to voters – only what they were feeling.

"He was a socialist. That just means that he wanted everyone to be more equal," Mitzy said. She continued,

"That's why he didn't approve of some of the business people, because he said they were getting rich at the expense of the Jamaican poor, the real working people."

"Well ... I guess that's why they didn't vote for him," I added.

Another friend quickly ran with this reasoning.

"And he especially didn't like the foreign bauxite companies because they were sending their money overseas.

Jamaica wasn't benefiting as much as it should from these foreign companies being here. That's why he introduced the bauxite levy."

Bernadette, who was mostly silent and did not participate much in our discussions on a regular basis, said,

"And don't forget that Manley taught us positive things like 'self-reliance' to help us reduce dependence on outside countries."

Now everyone started talking at the same time. Bernadette did not want us to miss the fact that Manley was a good man, but in the minds of some people, he was now vilified because of his political policies.

"Plus, he was also popular with other developing countries like ours," she insisted.

That last point sounded great, but I was not sure we appreciated what it meant. What we knew was that for some Jamaicans the excitement of Manley's speeches about socialism had worn off. The masses felt that some of his policies were not working out. Lately, their day-to-day existence had not improved much under his watch.

Melody jumped into the conversation at this point.

"Every night the news is showing us that people are going through difficulties across the country. They can't buy the food they need because prices are going up and up; a lot of these people aren't even working."

She was right. For a few years, the government was clamping down on the number of imported items entering the country. This was to control spending and manage the foreign exchange scarcity, the news had said.

Manley's government had also promoted the development of local manufacturing and agriculture to encourage a system they called 'import substitution'.

"So, what was the main reason for Mr Seaga beating Mr Manley then?" Alice asked. She was looking directly at me, so I spoke up.

"Well," I said, "instead of things getting better for us, they were getting worse."

I did not have to see that on TV; I was speaking from experience.

The economy had slowed down drastically under the policies the government had pursued. What I saw on TV was that when persons went to the shops and supermarkets, the shelves were almost empty – there was never enough rice, flour or sugar for everyone. I heard that shoppers were getting into fistfights trying to grab the last bag of any of these things they could find.

"Well, that wouldn't happen if we were making our own goods instead of importing them," Bernadette snuck in, to counter my point.

"But we can't make enough flour, we don't grow rice and we send most of our sugar to England and then buy back sugar from other countries. In the first place, the country is not earning enough money to buy the things we cannot make here and secondly, the government has restricted how much of those items can come into the country," Melody stated emphatically.

That may have been one of the main dilemmas under socialism. We were giving up basic foreign goods, which we could not afford anyway, but neither could we produce them locally.

The Jamaican masses no longer cared that Manley had given them free education and other social benefits, such as greater access to land and affordable homes. As far as they could see, the country had run out of money. Manley was unable to sustain democratic socialism. So, the eligible populace from across all classes and backgrounds in the island – including most of his former die-hard supporters – voted him out of office, handing the reins of leadership to the JLP and Edward Seaga.

The bell rang for our history class.

Our history teacher was out sick. The moment was a gift, as we needed to wrap up our discussion on what was now a historic saga.

Someone decided to switch from Manley to the new prime minister and the future he had promised.

"But Sanaa, yuh think Seaga can really make the country normal again?" It was, of course Miss Troubleshooter, Alice. She asked a good question.

But I really had not expected her to ask her follow-up question. It was always such a point of contention in the public domain.

"Is he even a true Jamaican?" she pressed.

Some Jamaicans did not trust Seaga, and it was not because he was of Lebanese descent and different in ethnicity from much of the population – after all, as our motto proclaims, we are 'Out of Many, One People'. No, there were rumours that he was really an American citizen posing as a Jamaican because of his family links.

"Yes Alice," I said, "but he was born overseas."

"So … if he was born overseas, how come you're saying he's Jamaican?" Bernadette asked.

"Because," I said, "his parents were Jamaicans. They came back to Jamaica with him when he was just three months old and he grew up here. He attended Wolmer's Boys' School."

Seaga had, on numerous occasions, defended his right to hold a spot in parliament. He had given up his American citizenship, so that made him eligible to be a Jamaican Parliamentarian and hence, to vie to become Prime Minister of Jamaica.

To deal with this issue, the Agency for Public Information (API), the government's publicity arm for keeping us updated about their programmes, had a feature on Mr Seaga. It was aired immediately after he won, as if they wanted to clear up the misunderstanding of his citizenship before he was sworn into office. It showed his family background and his political accolades, leading up to his victory. I silently thanked API for coming to my rescue.

Though Seaga was a typical, looking Lebanese, he was not a merchant like most other Jamaicans of similar background. Rather, he was a full-time politician with an interest in the poor and their social development. In parliament, he wore neatly fitting dark suits, his straight black hair slicked back. During the campaign period, when not in parliament, he always appeared more relaxed in green polo shirt and slacks, ringing his bell – the party's political symbol – his wailing high-pitched voice haunting, as he declared that the country would face doom if the people re-elected the PNP. Most Jamaicans began believing they needed Seaga by then, whether they were Arab, White, Black, Chinese, Indian, of mixed race or ethnicity. He seemed to offer a safe and alternative politics.

"So how did he really convince so many people to vote for him?" Alice asked.

"That's a tough one; he definitely wasn't as popular as Manley before all of this confusion," Bernadette spoke up matter-of-factly. She continued,

"I used to hear my parents and their friends talking that he was working with America's Central Intelligence Agency (the CIA), to prevent communism from taking over Jamaica. They said that the CIA helped plan all the demonstrations the JLP organized before the elections."

"Bernadette, yuh sure that is not hearsay?" Melody asked.

"Nobody can prove that, so let's stick to what we know." She added almost warningly.

This was a ticklish point Bernadette had raised. Based on what I had read in a magazine I found in the library, the US no doubt had a strong interest in the direction of Jamaica's politics at the time. Those were the days of the Cold War between the Western world (unofficially led by the US) and the Communist bloc of countries like the Soviet Union and China. And, at the time, Jamaica actually had a communist party, the Workers Party of Jamaica (WPJ). The WPJ was not gaining much traction, but was quite strident regarding the direction they believed the country should take to achieve economic and social development.

To make matters worse, Manley was keeping company with communist Cuba. Its dictator, Fidel Castro, was his close ally. The political pandemonium in Jamaica and our affiliations were of concern to America – given their stance against communism; it clashed with their democratic creed. Geographically, both Cuba and Jamaica are in America's backyard. As Manley's friendship with Castro strengthened, the relationship between Jamaica and her benefactor, Uncle Sam, became strained. America was not pleased with Jamaica. It was more than a mild case of a geopolitical 'cyass-cyass', it was a security concern for them. For, which country would be comfortable surrounded by its archenemy and friends?

While these thoughts swam around in my head, I heard Melody making a bold suggestion.

"Bernadette," she said in a very mature voice, "whether we want to accept it or not, Mr Seaga won the election because Jamaicans believed we were on the brink of becoming a communist country – like Cuba. The only way to switch things back was by switching out the politicians.

"And," she continued with authority, ". . . that is the main reason why people voted for Seaga. They wanted things to go back to normal."

As Seaga often said to his critics after stating his facts, "Argument done."

Melody may have been on to something.

Supporters of the quixotic Michael Manley had named him 'Joshua' because of his radical plans to improve their lives and lead them out of the wilderness of poverty. Now they no longer believed that Manley could close the gap between them and those he referred to as "... the privileged elite".

That wrapped up our discussion as the afternoon bell rang, signalling the end of our very informative session.

Despite the change in the country's political leadership and ideological direction after October 1980, economically, things remained difficult.

When it was his turn to lead the country, Seaga had to face the hard facts. There was not going to be much 'deliverance' as he had promised. The country was broke. The Jamaican dollar had suffered rapid devaluation against the US currency and Seaga needed to borrow money to keep on going. He haggled with the international lending institutions for low interest rate loans – particularly the International Monetary Fund (IMF), with which Manley had only months before ended a borrowing relationship, cutting off a much needed source of cash.

The IMF's 'take it and do that' approach to lending,

known as 'conditionality', meant that Seaga had to take their advice along with their money, and the country was managed under a tight programme of structural adjustment dictated by the lenders. Seaga was hoping to plug the gaps in the public budget. The programme required strict planning and supervision of government spending, but this approach reduced spending on social services. Most Jamaicans did not receive these measures well – even those who were sceptical of democratic socialism.

Even though money was not yet flowing in the economy and things were still rough, the general 'vibes' in the country improved after the 1980 election.

But the changes in the country had very little impact on my private world.

5

An Element of Colour

AFTER THE FALSE START TO MY friendship with Mark, and after the country embarked on its new path, I decided it was time for me to put all my negative personal experiences behind me.

My life slowly started to open, like a flower reaching towards the sun. A new energy emerged from within me and I went back to being more like the me I knew before the despair – friendly and outgoing.

Mom was actually living closer to her girlhood community in Shortwood, where she had grown up with her mother. This allowed her to reconnect with some of the friends she had gone to school with, who still lived in that area. There was Mrs Chin, with whom Mom had attended infant school at St John the Evangelist, off Mannings Hill Road, who now lived one avenue away from us. Then, just two doors down was the buxom Ms Bent, who was a sister of one of Mom's best friends from her intermittent attendance at Shortwood Practicing School (having broken her attendance there when she had moved away to live with her dad).

Mom also met and became friends with Mrs Smith, the wife of one of her childhood friends who was now a furniture manufacturer. It was good to see her laughing again when these women would come by sometimes to have afternoon tea or just to chat. I cherished those moments – seeing my mom take "just five minutes" as she would say, for relaxing and socializing. She was able to take some time with friends as she had rehired someone to help her with the household tasks, so she could focus on sewing.

Mommy would also take breaks to attend Sunday morning service. On a Wednesday night, she would go to prayer meeting – stopping briefly along the way to say "howdy-do" to her old friend, Mr Smith. Then, both she and Mrs Smith would walk down to church together.

Sometimes Mom went on a quick trip downtown, where she could get some bargains for the house and supplies for her trade – and I suspect some much-needed time for herself. From there she would go to Franklin Town to collect the rent from her father's property, as she was his only child living in Jamaica. Apart from that, my mother's life was still about work, though not with its former gruelling urgency. She even found time to teach a couple of young women from the church and community how to sew as she now had more time to engage others – despite her commitments.

I remember one amusing occasion when she decided to go out on a Saturday at about midday. Mom was already dressed in her favourite floral dress, bag on shoulder, about to leave for downtown when we heard our front gate open. We were in the living room and could see very clearly from there if anyone was at our gate or in our front yard. Looking out towards the gate, we spied Ms Bent strolling down towards our grilled verandah unannounced apparently hoping for a little chat. Ms Bent was unmarried and had no children. When I first met her, she had a live-in male companion. Now she lived alone with a few guard dogs as her sole company. She often expressed how lonely she was, except for the summer months when her nephew would visit from America.

Ms Bent's untamed salt and pepper hair was blowing in the wind towards our direction, as if waving hello. She was always well put together even if going only two doors up the avenue. For this visit, she was sporting Bermuda shorts, kitten-heel sandals and a white t-shirt, which strained against her full bosom. To complete her outfit, she wore goggle-like sunglasses, as it was a very sunny afternoon.

As Ms Bent came closer to the house, Mom looked almost petrified,

"Oh my God," she said, "I love her dearly, but I have to leave now to catch the stores before they close; just tell her I not here."

Mom then dropped down on her hands and knees, making a speedy exit from the living room. Head low, she navigated her way to the kitchen, through the laundry room and out the backdoor. Only then did she straighten up to climb through a narrow aperture in our back fence and on to a little track behind our house that led to the main road. From there, she could catch her bus to Parade, the central shopping area in downtown, Kingston. She could not afford any delays.

When Ms Bent came into the house, she was only able to catch a whiff of Mommy's Avon Topaz perfume.

I laughed all afternoon at my mother's quick thinking in extricating herself from that ill-timed social call.

But generally, home was now fun. The gloom was gone.

I experimented with baking and cooking and entertained friends and family on weekends and holidays. Tony was my biggest supporter, cheering me on in my role as resident chef and gorging on any food or pastry I produced, regardless of how they turned out. The first time I tried to make an Easter bun, I did not consult a cookbook. Instead, I picked my mother's brain for her grandmother's recipe.

No one recognized my bun for what it was, but Tony remained faithful to the cause. Laughingly, he assured me,

"Sanaa, the bun is not too bad yuh nuh. Good try. It can eat, just a bit tough; nothing a little butter won't help."

"Thanks Tony, I know I can rely on yuh to grade my baking," I retorted.

He continued eating the bun over the Easter weekend, right down to the very last slice.

Now a young adolescent, Tony was also a good cook, as Mom ensured we all learned by cooking alongside her on weekends. Eventually we would take over the cooking – alternating on weekends so Mom could relax.

Apart from being in the kitchen a lot, I also spent a good deal of time reclining on the bench under the Bombay mango tree in our front yard. There, I could feel the waning heat of the afternoon sun streaming between its leaves, teasing out the jumbled-up words from my head on to paper, and into some semblance of poetic structure. Sometimes I would sit under the tree and study or just read novels borrowed from any source I could find. I had grown to appreciate solitude and I found this under my tree. It was my very own cocoon for hatching new dreams. There I felt renewed hope for my life as I had left the memory of my father behind me where it belonged – in my past. I rarely, if ever at all, thought about him.

It was perhaps the best time of my youth because in the middle of it, I met someone special. Jay.

Pardon the cliché here but we were friends before he became my first real love.

After briefly distancing myself from a God I thought had distanced himself from me, my Christian faith was back in top gear. Not only was I participating fully in my church again, I was also involved in a church-based youth club called Sunshine Centre. The Centre promoted a wholesome Christian lifestyle and networking.

That is where I met Jay.

It was on a Saturday evening in the early summer of the year I had gone to Grand Cayman.

I had just arrived at the Centre wearing a crisp lavender denim skirt with a complementary lavender and white striped top I had purchased on my overseas trip. White strappy sandals completed the outfit. I stood in the open front yard, looking to see if my friends had arrived.

"Sanaa," I heard someone call my name. I did not recognize the voice – but whomever it belonged to made my name sound sweet.

I turned in the direction of the voice and my eyes collided with those of a young man I vaguely remembered seeing the week before. He motioned for me to come over to where he was sitting on the steps leading up to the old house we used for the meetings.

I did not know who he was.

I did not move.

My new acquaintance got up and started walking towards me, smiling broadly. He was a bit on the skinny side and I guessed that he was just shy of 6 feet in height. He was dressed in full denim overalls with a white cotton shirt on the inside, sleeves rolled up. White sneakers completed his attire. As my new acquaintance hurriedly walked over and came closer to me, the voices of the other young people waiting for the session to begin were suddenly inaudible. It was an indication that I was about to meet someone special.

"Hi, I'm John – but you can call me Jay, that's J-a-y," my new acquaintance said in a husky voice, as we came face to face.

Chuckling at his introductory joke, I saw that Jay's eyes were intensely dark as he stared into mine. He was of mixed Jamaican descent – and it was obvious he had not trimmed his curly hair for a while as it was long and more than a little unkempt, completing his hippie look.

"I'm Sanaa," I replied, barely smiling up at him, and wondering how he knew my name.

"I know," Jay said, "I just called you, remember?"

I blushed. He was not the best-dressed guy around, but he was ruggedly handsome, and obviously very amusing. He had an aura that set him apart from other young men I knew. I forgot about looking for friends as Jay and I took adjacent seats in the area set up for worship.

We spent the evening sharing about ourselves between the breaks in the informal Saturday evening programme.

"So, what do you do Sanaa?" Jay asked in his smooth fashion. Then he answered his own question,

"Hmm, let's see, I think you're still a high school student."

"Yes," I said. "You're right. I'm actually finishing up – at St Andrew High."

"Oh . . . St Andrew, my sister went to that school . . . but I'm not sure you knew her. She would've been a few years ahead of you.

"And I'm just about to enter university back home. . . in Canada," he added.

Jay did not live in Jamaica but was here on summer vacation. His family had migrated to Canada during the onset of economic and political instability in Jamaica in the mid-1970s. That explained his constant switching between Standard English and Jamaican dialect, his use of the latter to underscore his points.

By the end of the evening, I found out that Jay's full name was John Stanley. He was the coolest guy ever – multi-dimensional. He was passionate about life and rebellious (in a good way). He was well read and had an opinion on almost everything. And he liked playing football and played the clarinet.

We clicked.

Despite his upcoming departure, Jay and I got to know each other well in the short space of a few weeks. He was like my mirror image (except for my brooding). I could not believe that someone like myself existed in the form of the opposite sex! We spoke about any and everything. He taught me about life in the First World, ". . . you work hard but there are rewards," Jay said. And I filled him in on politics and culture in Jamaica, telling him, "Oh . . . I know about change and understanding what it is to live from day-to day without certainty of resources . . . " All without mentioning my father. It was too early.

I knew that soon Jay would be going back home, but when he left one month later, I was very glum. I could not understand why I would meet someone so special, someone I could be open with, who could not be here with me. I thought,

"Why Lord?"

A real connection had sparked between us and we both hoped that we could continue to build a friendship. Jay had made an impact on my life in a short time; he was always positive and thinking big.

I was happy to have met such a deep and kind soul so unexpectedly towards the end of my scrambled adolescence. I was going to miss him.

Soon after Jay returned to Canada, he sent his address to me through a contact at the Centre, asking that I write to him. I was glad to hear from him. During our goodbye, we had somehow forgotten to exchange addresses!

After that, there were many letters between us. There was no declaration of love from either of us in any of our exchanges for a long time, but we both had a strong desire to keep connected. The truth is, when I realized that I had more than friendly feelings for Jay, the poetry began flowing in his direction. The love I wrote of remained my secret. I could not risk sharing the poems with him. He was such a dear friend. I did not want to lose that.

Jay's talk about starting university inspired me to have a meaningful plan for my life. I refocused on my education, recognizing that I had wasted some time and had not made any specific plans towards a career. When I was in primary school, I had told my mom that I wanted to be a lawyer. I parked that dream when my mom tried to explain exactly what a lawyer does in a way that she thought I could understand.

"Sometimes lawyers must tell untruths in court to help people when they are in trouble with the police," she had said.

With that limited information on the legal profession, I wondered if I could be both a Christian and a lawyer.

After that exchange with my mom, I had no specific career goal – except, maybe, to become a professional dancer. I loved dancing and, as a child, I had wanted to learn ballet and tap dancing. My favourite movies were the old Hollywood musicals laden with singing and dancing, often shown on 'Sunday Matinee', by JBC TV at about 11am. Or, maybe eventually, I thought, I could go into politics and help to fix the things that had gone wrong in Jamaica and improve the lot of the poor. Surely, that was Christian-like. I also had ideas about meeting the new prime minister, Edward Seaga – he was such a strong man, powerful in redirecting our history. I would ask him:

"Did you have any secret fears when speaking up against democratic socialism?

"What are your plans for unifying Jamaica after it was split by ideological differences?

"How will you preserve the legacy of Michael Manley – particularly as it relates to free education for all Jamaican children?"

And finally, I would ask, "How are you going to help the families who have lost loved ones because of politics?"

This final question was particularly important for me.

At school, we had to digest the sad news of the death of one of our Student Council leaders during the pre-election period. She was caught in the crossfire of opposing sides in her community. The Magazine Committee asked me to write a poem as a tribute from the school to her. My thoughts were that she was plucked from us – like a rose-bud; not yet fully bloomed.

The incident made our young hearts heavy and led me to reconsider my career choices.

I could not entertain the idea of getting to politics. I wanted to do something my mother would endorse. No, I would have to go into some other mainstream career.

I was determined to make up for my under-performance in high school. So I decided to pursue a professional three-year college diploma in early childhood education, after completing one year of sixth form. I had focused on commercial subjects, but realized that accounting was not what I wanted to pursue. I had done a career aptitude test and education was one of the suggested fields – this along with law, hospitality and journalism. Given my liberal arts focus, I could pursue a career in any of these disciplines. I found my answer when one of my neighbours asked me to tutor his seven-year-old daughter who was behind in her lessons. My little student was very stubborn, but I enjoyed the experience – as much as I had while playing school with Tony and Prudence when we were younger. Obviously, I would play the teacher; this always gave me the opportunity to show-off how much more I knew than they did in any subject area. I had loved it when they were in awe of me. Teaching was looking attractive.

I decided to discuss the teaching option with Mom after talking to a church colleague who had attended Shortwood Teachers' College. She gave it rave reviews.

"Mommy, what yuh think of me going to Shortwood . . . to train as a teacher? I checked it out and I think I'll be able to qualify for entry."

I was short of a recommended subject for entering my programme of choice, but I was still hoping to skip the qualifying preliminary year.

"Shortwood is a good college; teaching is a good profession," Mom said, ". . . but it must be expensive!"

"It's not so expensive," I added quickly, "just some small fees. I can live there too for not much more money."

"Well . . . yuh know I have no money for anything extra, but I will support yuh how I can. Why yuh don't ask Aunt Nell to help?"

"Oh . . . Ok. I will ask her."

I said this nodding my head in agreement and visualizing how this plan could come alive.

Nell was Mom's younger sister in Brooklyn, New York. She was always kind to me, sending clothing for us and funds to assist Mom from time-to-time. Mom had never allowed me to ask any of her family members for assistance before; so, I gathered she perceived this move to go to college as an important decision.

I made my application to Shortwood Teachers' College.

On acceptance, I met with the principal and explained how I planned to get the recommended subject while covering first year instead of wasting an entire year at the preliminary level. My negotiation strategy was successful. I went straight into the Early Childhood Education Programme. The follow-up plan was to use the diploma to matriculate to university for higher studies.

When I got to college, I found that my abilities were intact. Shortwood was a good experience. I received more than a teaching diploma, as the institution focused equally on developing our professionalism and decorum.

College life also jolted me further into maturity. Being away from home, even if only walking distance away, forced me to take full responsibility for the direction of my life. College living also gave me some degree of autonomy. I often looked forward to time alone on weekends to get some work done, read or just enjoy the novelty of having a bedroom to myself, whenever my roommate went home for an entire weekend.

At the end of my first year of college, a sad thing happened at home. My grandmother, who had come to stay with us, fell suddenly ill. It was strange to see her ill because she was a fit woman. Only Grandma's silver hair gave away that she was an elderly woman, and this was because she refused to dye it. Though in her seventies, she was very active, and this had helped her to maintain her well-proportioned body. She walked to her church, Rehoboth on Constant Spring Road, more than once per week and kept active in the yard, always trying to revive our rose garden.

Mommy, with Gary driving, rushed Grandma to the University Hospital early on the Sunday morning after she fell ill. I expected her to return home on the same day, but she did not. Grandma died during surgery. I was close to her since I was a little girl and her death was not only shocking, but also upsetting. I will always be grateful for her and particularly, her last motivating words to me on that weekend before she died, when I told her I was successful in my first year-exams.

"Sanaa," she said, smiling though her pain, "That's good! I know yuh'll continue to do well."

I have such fond memories of her.

When I was in Grade 1, my grandmother appeared at my school one day – a first. Class was on break and we were playing in the schoolyard. Waving at me, my grandmother headed straight to my classroom. Apparently, she was looking for my teacher. In a very short time, she returned saying,

"Come, Sanaa, pack up yuh books."

"Yuh going to Grade 2!"

It was an instant promotion to Grade 2. Grandma held my hand and walked me to the second grade. There, she presented me with a note from the principal to my new and quite bewildered teacher. Apparently, she had also stopped at the principal's office before visiting my Grade I teacher.

On her first stop, she had persuaded the principal to send me to Grade 2 because she thought I was too advanced for my class. The truth is that I had spent almost a year at home due to illness when I should have been in Grade 1. However, I did not miss out on much of my education, as Brenda gave me lessons at home.

Grandma was often very mysterious too. She had not discussed with her daughter that she was coming to live with us. She just locked up her little house, moved in her clothes piece-by-piece, stayed longer and longer with each visit, and then never left.

When Grandma started staying with us full-time, Gramps, our boarder, was just on her way out and their tenure in our home overlapped briefly. Gramps became the most angelic old woman you could find, as she knew my grandmother was a serious Christian. Many evenings while they both sat on the verandah, Grandma would often speak to her about the goodness of the Lord. Gramps, in the spirit of the moment, would recite some relevant Bible verses she could remember, even though she had not been to church for many years.

Apart from the gardening, which was her hobby, Grandma's self-assigned duties were washing up the dishes and feeding the pets. When in a cooking mood, she would prepare ripe banana fritters or *polenta,* commonly known as turned cornmeal, (which was seasoned cornmeal cooked down with water into a tight paste). This one-pot meal was a staple for low-income households in Jamaica. Grandma would be quite disappointed when there were no takers for the turned cornmeal. I did not like either of these dishes but would try to appease her by eating at least one of the fritters, whenever she made them. Tony, of course, would participate heartily in Grandma's banana fritters feast.

Grandma might not have been the best cook, but she was a good grandmother and a kind person – always willing to listen to us, while getting in a few stories of her own. How could I not feel shaken at the death of a grandmother who had looked out for me the way she had?

I cried for months after Grandma's sudden death. When my grandfather had passed away, it had also been a sad event. He too had held a special place in my heart, but it was not as heartrending, as he had been ailing for some time. With the right treatment, Grandma could have been around for many years, I believe. But she had been depending on home remedies to cure her ailment and had waited too long before getting medical attention. None of us had any idea how ill Grandma was, because she kept very busy until a couple of days before going to the hospital, when the pain apparently became unbearable.

After Grandma's departure, home continued to be like a refueling station, with persons who needed my mother's nurturing constantly coming in to be around her. Before I finished college, Errol had a daughter, his only child, and his visits with us resumed on Sundays; this time with his family of three. It was clear that he wanted his daughter to be close to her grandmother, hence the weekly visits.

Then there was Uncle Herbert, my mother's uncle (Grandma's brother) who had come to live nearby. His daughters were overseas and so he stayed close to his niece for company and some warm meals. Uncle Herbert would come by almost every day, always dressed in his long-sleeved shirts as if he were still working; despite being over 80 and long retired. He was a jokester and kept us amused whenever he was there. His commentaries on the highly-promoted boxing matches between Mike Tyson and his endangered opponents were particularly funny.

"Lynette, who yuh cheering for tonight?" He would tease Mom.

"Don't tell mi is Mike Tyson? I hope him don't tek off anybody ears or other body parts tonight. Heh, heh!" Uncle Herbert led the laughter for his own joke.

My mom, being the family matriarch, loved having everyone around her – those who visited and those who stayed – including her teasing uncle. I took the opportunity to study the personal nuances each brought to the family hub, while dreaming of the ideal family I wanted to have in the future.

Throughout my college years, Jay and I stayed in touch. He knew all the details of my life and I knew the details of his. Our friendship grew stronger and when he came back almost two years after we became friends, I was very happy to see him.

We spent some quality time together during that visit. I met his parents briefly when I went by his grandmother's house where they were all staying. I did not interact with his father, but his mother was very warm and seemed spunky. I did not get to talk much with her when we met, as Jay and I were heading to the movies at Carib Cinema. We did not think of it as a date; we were not in a relationship. We were just best friends hanging out.

Early the following morning, Jay visited me at home after completing his run. He had turned up unannounced, but it was a pleasant surprise. He met my mom and of course, she had to question him a bit.

"So, Jay, how yuh doing? How is university?"

"I'm well Ms Mullings and university is fine but not always easy. But I'm coping."

"So how are you Ms Mullings? I hope Sanaa is not sending up your pressure in any way!" Jay was looking straight at me with a mischievous twinkle in his eyes.

"No Jay, she's a good girl!" My mother said this sincerely, at the same time mentioning that she had some sewing to do and wishing Jay a good day.

Jay had plans to go to the beach with some other friends that day.

This time his visit would last only for a few weeks, so we had to make the most of it and he wanted to know what else we were going to do together before he left.

Here was someone who listened to every word I said, every single syllable I uttered, as if each were a musical note flowing from my lips. He did not brush aside any of the ideas that I shared with him as stupid or far-fetched. I was very grateful for his friendship and I knew if he lived here, we would be inseparable. But Jay had to return home and again the parting was agonizing. I wanted him to stay and be my constant inspiration.

Before he left, I decided to tell Jay how much he meant to me.

"I'm not sure why, Jay, but I've been thinking about you more and more over the last few months; just missing you."

Jay stared into my eyes as he always did when I was speaking, but this time he was not smiling. He looked concerned, then said seriously:

"Sanaa, if I was here, I know we would have more than a friendship, because I care for you so much and I know you feel the same way about me." He continued,

"But the distance between us just won't help us sustain a relationship of that kind. You know I don't do anything halfway."

I nodded that I understood. Jay and I hugged, tightly.

He was a gentleman and I was a lady, so we did not fan the flames of affection. When he left, I fully accepted that loving Jay would not help me in times of loneliness, as he was so far away, as he had pointed out.

I would have to let go of my growing feelings for Jay.

But that was not so easy to do and I continued to long for the day when distance would no longer come between us.

Then, briefly, fate seemed to be on my side. A few months after returning to Canada, Jay wrote to say that he was planning to return to live in Jamaica after completing his studies.

I was thrilled!

However, my excitement was soon muted by his next letter. He was not coming home alone. He now had a girlfriend. He had mentioned in passing that he was dating a girl of Jamaican descent. She was also coming. Jay was saying in this letter,

"The lady I mentioned in my last letter – that's real now."

"What?" I thought, "He isn't coming home to me?" Then when that sank in, I thought, "Oh God, no! What type of friendship are we going to have if Jay's girlfriend is the jealous type?"

A few months later, I met her. She came ahead of Jay and enrolled in The University of the West Indies, 'UWI'. This would give her some lead time to help her to adjust to living here before Jay arrived. Jay had asked me to make her feel at home and help her to adapt to the culture. Born in Jamaica, she had left when she was an infant and did not know much about the island.

I loved Jay, so I did the noble thing and tried to be a friend to his girlfriend. She was easy to like. Of course, with her not knowing my feelings for him, she would go on and on about him: "Jay said this . . ." or "Jay did that . . ."

I often wanted her to shut up about him, but I had to be polite.

Soon Jay's girlfriend admitted that studying here in Jamaica was more challenging than she had thought it would be. She left before the end of her first year. After she left, I breathed a sigh of relief. Thank God, because I doubted how much longer I would have been able to keep up my pretense – feeling the way I did about Jay. And then, I wondered if her return to Canada would affect Jay's decision to relocate to Jamaica. I would wait to see.

My college years were ending, and I continued to meet young men who showed an interest in me, but none of them could get through to me the way Jay had. None of them moved me the way Jay did, though some of them became very good friends.

Even though I was an adult now, Mom was not ready to allow me to go on real dates. The guy friends had to come to my home if they wanted to spend time with me. Those who came to dinner or just dropped in unknowingly became the subject of ongoing assessment. My mom would say she liked this one or that one or, "Be careful yuh know, such and such a person going to grow on yuh." She did not know that I was saving my love for Jay, though he seemed to have moved on with his life.

6

Don't Ask, Don't Tell

DISTANCE.

That was still the one thing keeping Jay out of my life. The relationship with his Jamaican-Canadian girlfriend had ended.

My only comfort was his impending return home.

But it was small comfort, as I had witnessed and shared in the heartbreak of family and friends who were falling out of love. I just did not understand this love thing. One story that challenged my faith in love was that of my older brother Gary.

Gary and I were never very close. I'm not sure if it was because of the seven-year age gap between us. We look a lot alike – both of us leaning more physically in resemblance to our father, having his narrow eyes and dark skin tone. Gary did not quite get our father's height but, at 13, he had an impressive growth spurt and thereafter grew to an average height and frame.

When he became a teenager, while we were still living in Hagley Park, he started staying out late on the road with the boys there and was generally disobedient to Mom. I remember many clashes between them when Mom came home late from work and Brenda had no idea where Gary was. Then they would go looking for him and all three of them would return together, with Gary tugging his bicycle behind him. Mom often failed miserably at trying to discipline Gary with blows. He was slippery.

Once, she stood on a chair and asked Brenda to catch Gary and hold him steady, so she could give him a good flogging. Gary, by then taller than both, outmaneuvered them. Mom got one blow in that ricocheted off Gary's elbow before he wrestled free from Brenda. He then dashed into his room and ran straight under his single bed.

"Brenda, how yuh mek him escape?" Mom hissed her teeth.

She followed immediately behind him and quickly pulled the bed from the wall. Gary's head bobbed up in the space between wall and bed and Mom forcefully pushed the bed against the wall, hoping to knock him out.

Gary was quicker than Mom. He rolled out from under the bed and darted pass her, laughing.

Irritated by this behaviour, Mom gave up the chase.

"I'm warning yuh," she said to a happy-go-lucky Gary, "I going to tell yuh father about the staying out late and the bad behaviour."

I am not sure she followed through with this threat, as I never at any time heard my father telling Gary off.

As Gary became an older adolescent, he settled down.

He became disciplined in his approach to schoolwork and he stayed inside the house a lot and started reading western novels. His favourite novels were by Louis L'Amour, an American writer. When he passed his Grade 9 Achievement Test at 14 or 15 to enter a traditional high school, Gary started studying even harder. He was now determined to make something of his life, I guess. He never shared with me at that time what he wanted to become but it was clear that he had a plan. This new studiousness was a big change from when he was younger and it meant a change for me too.

Before he became studious, Gary's idea of showing me brotherly attention was every so often pressing down a pillow over my head to cut off my air supply. I would spend what seemed like more than a few seconds wriggling my way out of that hold; then suddenly, he would release me. I would come up gasping for air. That was Gary's idea of fun. I started growing my fingernails as a weapon of defence against Gary's attacks – flashing them like daggers whenever he came near me. It worked perfectly.

After the pillow was no longer an effective means of intimidating me, and I guess too because he was now more mature, Gary gave up on antagonizing me for a while. Notwithstanding the scaling back of the 'ragging', he gave me a not-too-complimentary nickname – *Day Ghost.* That I could live with. What I could not live with was when he began blaming me for our father's aborted visits to our home after that night of my shaming.

I'm not sure to what extent the falling out between my father and me had affected Gary. By then he was out of school and had completed his stint in the National Youth Service programme. He was of voting age, a grown young man, but he actively censured everything I did from then. Perhaps he had concluded that I was wayward and needed continuous rebuke.

Even my career choice after high school was a wrong decision in Gary's estimation. He was not amused that I had chosen to live the life of the 'luxury poor', by planning to study for three years instead of doing a quick six-month secretarial course to get a skill.

"Sanaa, when yuh going to start working and making contributions to the household?" he asked.

So, when Gary fell in love, we all exhaled. I was especially relieved, as he relaxed his policing of me. This is the amazing thing about the first phase of love: we are always so eager to have others share in our joy. Gary had a special joy to share with me, his sister.

"Sanaa, why yuh don't come with Janice and me to visit Daddy for the Independence weekend?"

I was dumbfounded!

I sucked in a deep breath.

How does one process an invitation to visit a father lost?

"Visit who?

"I didn't know I still have a father," I stated flatly.

"Where is he?"

"Stop the foolishness nuh!" Gary was getting impatient.

"Your father – our father – said yuh should come with me to Montego Bay."

"I didn't know him remember mi," I said matter-of-factly.

"Why him want mi around now, anyway?"

"I told him that yuh finish college, yuh nuh."

"Why yuh telling him mi business?"

There was a burning pang in my stomach. I wanted Gary to understand how I felt about my father's resurrection.

"I – don't – want – him – to know – anything – about – me."

"Well, he says yuh should come and I not going without yuh."

Gary kept up variations of this conversation with me for about two weeks until he succeeded in persuading me to go and visit my father in Jamaica's second city. He had enlisted Mom's help, knowing I would not say "No" to her.

All Gary wanted was for me to get back to my father. Despite my lack of interest, he gave me a rewind of what I had missed.

During the years I never saw my father, he was still living in Montego Bay and still visiting Kingston – still going about his regular business while being absent from my life! Up to that point, I had not even the slightest inkling that Gary had stayed in touch with our father, even as I pretended he was no more. Sometimes when our father came to Kingston, he and Gary would meet at the races.

The week before we left for Montego Bay, Gary had another surprise for me. He wanted to introduce me to a younger sister that he had just discovered – my father's youngest child. This was too much. I thought I was my father's youngest child – his only daughter. I was so angry with my dad for this new offence – for keeping my sister away from me when he was around – that I decided it was no use forcing sisterhood on her. I felt that was how my father wanted it to be, so I would respect his wishes.

The funny thing is that I had always wished I had a sister; but even funnier is that I grew up believing that Gary and I were my father's only children. That was obviously part of the myth that my father had created about his life. I wondered how much my mother knew about this and why she had helped to perpetuate the myth.

The pressure was intensifying. Trying to reconnect with someone who I had no feelings for after that night – someone I had declared dead on all the forms I had filled out in high school and while attending college – would be one of the most difficult steps I would ever take in my life. I dreaded the thought of facing this man. I no longer knew him. What would he be like? Did he still consider me a brat for stomping on his ego? Or had he forgotten what had transpired between us the very last time we saw each other?

Well, it seemed like the past was not going to be of any significance. The icy silence between my father and I unbelievably began to thaw a few days before I ventured down to see him. I spoke to him on the telephone Gary had handed me without warning.

Though he was dead to me, his image lay embedded in the recesses of my mind; tarnished by fury, but indelible. It resurfaced slowly, as if he were exhumed, when I heard his voice coming at me through the telephone receiver. It was the strangest thing. My father spoke in a tone that was so cordial and in such contrast to that night when he had thundered at me, seven years ago, that I briefly questioned the accuracy of my painful memory of the incident.

"Hi, darling," my dad said casually, as if we had last seen each other just the day before.

"Congratulations. I heard you graduated from college." There was a long uncomfortable pause and then,

"Why didn't you invite me to your graduation?"

"I didn't think of it," I replied. I really wanted to say, "I didn't know you were alive." However, I lacked the temerity.

"San, I hear you're coming down for Reggae Sunsplash with Gary," my father said.

Sunsplash, as we youngsters called it for short, was Jamaica's signature reggae 'rock' concert, held annually in the summer since 1978. People from all over the world who loved Jamaican music, including Jamaicans living abroad, would flock to Jarrett Park in Montego Bay to hear famous Jamaican bands like Third World perform live. Each day the concert went from dusk to dawn of the following day, when the sun literally splashed onto the grass of the concert grounds at sunrise.

"Yes. Can I bring a friend?" I had decided that having a friend with me would be useful in helping me to deal with any discomfort on this visit.

"What type of friend?"

"From college . . ."

He quickly figured out that it was a female friend, as I had attended an all-girls' college.

"Yes," I heard my dad saying, "I have enough space, you know – yes."

Wow . . . my great, big, awesome dad was back!

I was tempted to feel overjoyed. Apparently, I had redeemed myself by not dropping out of the school system after he had given up on me. I had even attained tertiary education. He may have been pleased with me, but I was far more pleased with myself for having done all of that without any help from him.

A nervous excitement was building inside me. I was not only beginning to look forward to the day when I would see my father again, but I was also excited at the thought of being able to introduce one of my friends to him for the very first time in my life. Yes, Karen was the perfect friend to help me get through this big moment. She had the sweetest spirit and the prettiest honey-brown eyes that could mesmerize even someone as cold as my father.

It was always a delight to be around Karen. Incidentally, she was the younger sister of another friend, Naomi. I had met them on separate occasions when I attended the Teen-Time Summer Camp while in high school. Naomi was a counsellor in training at the camp. I was 13 years old when we met. She stood out because she sported a very low Afro and had loads of panache. Naomi was everything I wanted to be as a young girl – articulate and sociable – and her warmth and sincerity drew me to her.

I adopted Naomi as an older sister and mentor when she started attending my church a few years later.

Karen and I became good friends during our college years. Mostly we spoke about Jay and her boyfriend, who was away at college. She shared with me some of the love letters he had written to her. I remember one letter written very creatively, starting from the centre of the paper and then expanding in a circular pattern to show how his love for her was growing daily.

The previous summer I had spent a week of fun with Karen at her family home in St Elizabeth. There, I ate my fill of watermelon, which was plentiful in that part of the island. Karen and I toured Santa Cruz and dined like tourists in a popular restaurant located in the humid, bustling town centre.

Karen and I had big plans for our lives, which included travelling. Before we returned from St Elizabeth, we decided that we should spend the rest of our long break in New York, where we both had relatives. Apart from the fact that we had no way of funding our trips, neither of us had a visa for the US but, we thought, that could be easily fixed.

Early one morning, a few days after returning to Kingston, we headed to the US Embassy. In those days, no appointment was needed – you literally just turned up with the relevant documents, took some visa pictures from any of the several photographers offering the service right outside the embassy gates, then waited to be interviewed. The hardest part was waiting in the long line of hopeful applicants, all of us praying that we would be blessed with the coveted US visa.

In preparation for our interview, we had rehearsed some answers to the questions we expected the US officials to ask us.

My turn at the interview window finally came after a very long wait. I smiled nervously as I walked up in a white handkerchief linen sundress Mom had hurriedly sewn.

"Good morning," I said brightly on approaching the window.

The interview was quick and seemed scripted.

"Ma'am, who are you visiting in the United States?" the consular officer asked, looking over his glasses at me.

"My Aunt Nell – Nellita Mullings," I responded. "She is a highly trained dietitian in Brooklyn," I added quickly in my best voice.

"And how long do you plan to stay in America?"

"Well as long as Aunt Nell will have me!" I replied with a grin.

"Do you have a job ma'am?"

"No," I shook my head, "I'm a college student."

"Sorry ma'am, but we cannot issue you a visa at this

time. But do feel welcome to apply when you are more settled."

I stood there for a few seconds as if I expected the gentleman to say "Gotcha" and change his mind. I could not believe he had decided my fate in such a cavalier manner. Then he handed me my passport after stamping it and scrawling a note on the inside of its back cover, looking beyond me to see his next applicant.

Karen did not get the highly sought-after US visa either. Apparently, they thought we did not have enough 'ties' to Jamaica (assets and commitments), to want to return after a US vacation. And that was where our touring ended that summer – at the embassy. We were young and free of obligations and easily fit the US Department of Immigration's profile of persons likely to 'run off' and become undocumented immigrants in America. The mass migration of the 1970s from Jamaica to the US had continued into the 1980s and while some who left were legal migrants, many were not.

Karen had emerged from her interview giggling, brushing off the turndown as "no big deal . . . after all, we could try again next year..."

That was Karen. She could ease the tension in any situation. I believe she was the only friend I had that Gary liked because of her genuine warmth.

It was a lovely summer – one with clear blue skies and lengthened days. You could not help but appreciate life in such a setting; it was conducive to reuniting with long lost loved ones.

We were on our way to Montego Bay; I sat in the back of Gary's car with the windows down. The sun gently stroked my skin. The weather was perfect for my inland vacation, I thought – a suitable graduation gift to myself.

In preparing for the three-hour journey to Montego Bay, I had taken a book to read but, as we left the city behind, I found my thoughts drifting. I did not make much progress into the story.

I was thinking about the changes in the political climate in the country.

The JLP government was now well into its second term after winning the 'snap election' in 1983 – so dubbed because it was called suddenly and way before their first term in office had officially ended. The PNP did not contest this election, primarily because the JLP was using the old voters' list since the last election in 1980.

Though the country had not yet recovered from the harrowing effects of the near-civil war leading up to the 1980 elections, there was evidence of decreasing political violence. The economy was improving, even if only slowly, and life was getting back to 'normal'. I suspect the government had wanted to capitalize on this mood in case things changed against their favour, hence the rushed election. Regardless of the disagreement between the government and the opposing party on this election, the political atmosphere in the country was markedly different than it was in 1980.

The journey was winding down.

As we approached the posh area in which my father resided in Montego Bay, I could no longer avoid thinking about what it would mean to reunite with him. Never did I expect to speak with him again, see him again, or what was even more extraordinary, spend time with him. This was a big deal for me. In all my childhood years, I had never ever spent time with my dad in his space. It still seemed almost unthinkable that this was about to change. Now I wondered what he looked like and how he would receive me – I looked nothing like I did the last time he saw me. I had grown a few more inches, had a womanly figure and I was more mature.

As we drove up to the gate and into his sloping yard, I could see my father standing at the top of the steps leading to the entrance of his house. It was not as I had imagined it would be. It was not a modern house but rather a cheerless ancient structure and I was not sure what period it reflected. Painted bone white with only a hint of bottle green around the wood-trimmed window frames, the house seemed unwelcoming, as if mocking me – as if it knew how much I had longed to be there when I was a child and how these desires had been thwarted.

My father stood watching as we drove up his driveway and disembarked from the car. He motioned to us and we climbed up the steps on which he had come halfway down to greet us. Gary spoke first.

"Hi Daddy, this is Janice."

"Pleased to meet you Janice; welcome and congratulations on the engagement!"

Janice blushed and said, "Thanks Mr Wallenston."

My father turned his eyes on me. I was more nervous than I had ever been, standing demurely in front of him after all these years. I was not sure what to expect. I was wearing my favourite outfit, a turquoise blue and white pinstriped shirtdress Mom had made for me, with a pair of patent white Mary Jane's. There I was, all grown up and looking chic, a college graduate and a well-rounded young woman, yet my father had no clue who I really was. Even worse, he had no idea of the pain he had caused when he turned his back on me. Yet, I felt that this was our real chance at being father and daughter again.

Our greetings were stiff.

"San, I hope you had a good ride down," he said, as though I belonged there.

"Yes . . . Daddy," I answered, the last word almost sticking in my throat.

There were no hugs or kisses to make up for lost years, but we got through the formalities.

We entered the house. Inside, my father continued on his quest to make conversation. My answers were mechanical. I was trying to focus on the moment; but he wanted me to fill him in with details about my life and also give him updates on my mom.

"So . . . San, what have you been up to, apart from college?" he asked.

"Nothing really," I answered, "Just church."

"How has your mother been doing?"

"Oh . . . she's sewing as usual and trying to make ends meet."

I decided to give myself a tour of his house – to get away from the questioning. I saw that my father kept his house well, but it lacked the lived-in feel of warmth and coziness. I was anxious to get a feel for his life, but as I went further into the house, its hardwood flooring squeaked with my every step, as if protesting my presence there.

I went into the room he had assigned to Janice and me and stayed there, the past years without him running through my mind. I heard bits and pieces of light conversation between himself and Gary drifting my way. They were talking about horse racing and other random things – none of which was of interest to me.

Later, after settling in and freshening up, we left for the Reggae Sunsplash concert and, though it was good, I was restless because of the lengthy band changes. Rock concerts were not my thing at the time, but I reminded myself that my main reason for being in Montego Bay was to see my father.

The next day was perfect – warm but not clammy. My dad took us to the famous Doctor's Cave Beach, and it seemed like with that single act he fulfilled all my childhood fantasies. But, I found it baffling that my dad did not introduce us to any of his associates that he greeted on the beach. I did not allow this to affect our near-perfect day; everything else was going well. We had a good time that evening too, taking family pictures and going out to see a play. But the good times lasted only until the following morning.

We were in my father's bedroom after breakfast, talking with him, when again my eyes wandered to a picture I had noticed there the day before. The picture, obviously taken some years ago, was of a young teenage boy whom I had never met, but whose picture clearly had good reason for prominent placement on my dad's chest of drawers. This young teenager strongly resembled Gary and me.

"Aah, Daddy . . . who is this?" I asked, somewhat hesitantly.

"Your brother . . ."

"How old is he?"

"Twenty-something . . ."

A quick calculation put the youngster in the picture as older than I was and younger than Gary. I could feel my stomach tightening in reaction to this news, but prodded on.

"So, where is he now?"

"In Florida," my dad answered sheepishly.

Before I could stop myself, I blurted out the question the moment was begging.

"How come I don't know him?"

Oops! That was a wrong move. In an instant, the shutters of secrecy fell over my father's eyes and I could not see what he was thinking as he gave me a hard, cold stare. I got no answer to my question.

My father walked away with Gary following him – both leaving me standing in the middle of the bedroom with my mouth agape. I would have to fill in the blanks without their help. I realized immediately that there was much more to my father's life than I knew. Neither would I know the full extent of how uninformed I was about his life, until much later.

Once again, I had broken the *Don't Ask, Don't Tell* rule my father lived by. At that moment, when he thought I was scrutinizing his life, my ratings swiftly slipped back to zero. The clock on my life ticked rapidly backwards to when I was 14. This time he did not rant at me, but I felt his reproach. Thereafter, my father dissected everything I said and decreed my ideas unworthy of utterance, just as he had done years before.

The remainder of my visit was tense. I wanted to leave the moment I realized that all I had left of my visit were dashed hopes of reconciliation with this man. It was as if a dark cloud had suddenly crept in front of the sun to once again cast a shadow over my life. I should not have been surprised.

Clearly, my father still saw himself as the victim of a daughter who had unrealistic expectations of him. My only redemption was that Karen had opted out of the trip at the last minute. It was only my brother and his wife to be who witnessed my mortification. Most painful of all was that I realized that my entire identity, whoever I thought I was up until that moment, was just a lie. I was not one of two or even three children my father had, but one of several.

Why did I not know of my father's other children? Did they know of me? Had they received more of my father's time and attention than I had over all those years? During the years that he was absent from my life, were they with him? All these questions invaded my mind as my identity foundation once again did a flip-flop – widening the gulf between my father and me. It was then that it hit me, that everything I knew about my father was second-hand information that I had received through my mom. My father had never ever shared any information with me about his siblings or parents, or about his experiences growing up or even anything about his adult life.

That night I could not sleep. My thoughts were crowded with images of the siblings I did not know and the father I thought I knew. I could not wait to get out of my father's space. I just wanted to bury the memory of him, once again.

When we left Montego Bay the following Monday afternoon, I quietly took my newfound knowledge of being part of an extended family back to Kingston with me. Perhaps it was not fair to my father's other children – but I assumed that while he had abandoned me, he had kept close to them. I was hurting because I felt left out of my own family. The hurt I felt was immeasurable and I kept it all inside. I had dared to face my father after years of silence between us and had only exposed my festering pain.

I did not discuss this sour episode with my mom until many years after, when I could speak about it freely without choking up. Still, to this day, I believe she unwittingly colluded with my father to create my false identity by following his *Don't Ask, Don't Tell* policy, which predicated his life.

Notwithstanding my annoyance at my mom's role in my 'forged' identity, I believe that was the first time in my life that I had fully appreciated the love and dedication she had bestowed on me. I rued the fact that I had so far taken my mother's love for granted. In the wrenching realization that I would never have my father's love or approval, the relationship I had with my mother grew to new heights. It was unshakable as there were no good reasons for me not to trust her, even though I had briefly questioned my trust in her. I reflected on how selflessly and gracefully my mother had undertaken the task of raising us, with only limited input from my father.

In the face of these revelations, I assessed my position regarding my father's view of his role in my life. It was about judging, rejecting and humiliating me, and I resolved to let go whatever emotional dregs I had from the memory of him, or so I told myself. I did not know then that my insatiable desire to gain my father's approval would ensure that I see him on just one more occasion during his lifetime.

Exactly one month after the failed reconciliation attempt in Montego Bay, I joined the workforce. That kept me busy and kept my mind averted from my father. But it appeared that at this time, there was a conspiracy between persons who had gone missing from my life in the late 1970s, to stir up my emotions.

On a very ordinary Sunday evening the following summer, we had some guests from overseas. It was Carmelita and three of her girls. Carmelita was home for a visit and had found Mom's listing in the telephone directory. She had called the day before to say that they were coming by, but when I saw them, I was not even sure how to act. For a moment, their presence catapulted me back in time. There they were, our old friends, standing in the centre of our living room as if they had never left Kingston. They were not staying for long and we all tried to fill in the missing years that we had not seen each other into just a few minutes. Most of the conversation was between Carmelita and my mother while the rest of us just looked on, smiling.

"Lyn, how have you been?" Carmelita inquired of my mother.

"Well," Mom said, "not too bad, yuh know. Things have been picking up, thank God. How things up there?" Mom was referring to Florida as if it was just up the road from us.

"Good, good so far," Carmelita responded. Then she went into who was working, who was going to college, and so on. Carmelita mentioned her sister, Olivia, who had also migrated with her family around the same time Carmelita left. They were also doing well.

Carmelita was her usual bubbly self – just obviously older. I did not remember her with graying hair before she left. I was relieved, however, that she had no fake American accent – no twang – to distort my memory of her.

Camellia, however, was different. Physically, she was basically the same – having retained her small frame, narrow hips and an almost flat chest. And she still had that unprocessed curly brown hair that complemented her bronzy complexion. But in other ways she was different, not just grown-up different; she was reserved and had an air about her. Camellia was not the talkative girl she used to be before leaving Jamaica and not much was said between us. We did not greet each other like long lost friends. We did not compare notes on how we had adjusted to our new lives over the last several years. Evidently, we were now vastly different persons, shaped by our own life-changing experiences during our early teenage lives.

I have no explanation as to why our families never stayed in touch after the migration; nor can I offer one as to why we did not rekindle our relationship after that visit. Their time with us was pleasant, though brief, and then they left without any indication as to when we might see them again.

After they left, it was reminiscent of the wistfulness I felt when they had said their first goodbyes nearly a decade ago. I thought about whether they regretted not sticking things out in Jamaica; if they regretted giving up the laid-back life they had had here. They were indeed part of the 'brain drain' Jamaica had experienced in the 1970s when the educated, professional classes had left in a mass exodus – many of them forced to take only the money from the quick sale of their valuables, not expecting to return.

But, I knew that for Carmelita's family and others like hers, no matter the benefits of the developed world, it had not been an easy decision to leave Jamaica, land of their birth.

There was little excitement in my life for a while, following the summer reunions. The only event on the horizon was Gary's upcoming marriage. The relationship had progressed very quickly and his wife to be was putting plans in place for an Easter wedding. She was pregnant. Mom would sew the bridesmaids' dresses and I would be the maid of honour.

Then, for some reason, they abandoned the plans for a church wedding. Instead, they had a civil wedding, with none of our family members present. After getting married, they moved in with us – straight into my mother's bedroom. The agreement was that Mom would sleep on the sofa until the newlyweds found a place of their own, within the next few weeks … or months.

Then the arguments between them started.

Gary's wife was not happy that they had to be living

in her mother-in-law's bedroom when they were about to start a family. And he was not happy that she could not be happy living with his family. Their romance was now like a humourless pantomime and my porous emotions soaked up all the emanating sadness floating around our house.

I poured it out on paper, as that was the only way I knew how to cope with trouble.

The couple eventually left for their new place in the suburban development of Portmore, about a month before their baby arrived. By then, based on what I had seen from the newlyweds, I was no longer enamoured with love.

If love was always going to cause pain, then perhaps it was pointless.

And so, my dream of being with Jay, my soulmate many miles away, became blurry, quelled by my disillusionment with love. Jay's last visit had been a few months after his girlfriend came to attend university and so we did not spend too much time together. Now they were no longer an item. While I had not seen him since then, we were still close. Jay remained my lifeline, despite being so far away.

Time passed but my life remained the same – characterized by the regular routines of life and the subliminal longing for love, forgiveness and approval.

My primary focus was to relieve my mom of some of the household bills.

I passed my free time in the evenings after work by reading, jogging at the football field by my old college or playing a little tennis with Karen. I worked hard to get fit and at perfecting my figure – though on the inside I nursed feelings of imperfection. I was finally beginning to win my secret battle with bulimia, which had started in my turbulent teenage years. The desire to purge my body after ingesting each meal was receding. Having some success and rekindling my dreams for the future helped me to get over some of the grief I had formerly known in my life. But, I still was not completely over the fact that I had fallen out of grace with my father not just once, but twice.

Weekends were about church. I was not as self-absorbed as it may seem. Rather, I was very involved with my cell group at church. These were small groups formed among the members, designed to foster closer fellowship and strengthen our faith. Our group was very diverse – a blend of young, middle-aged and older people – but we all had fun together. We went to the beach, volunteered at a children's home or just hung out together and played games on Saturdays. Naomi was also in this group and I cultivated some other lasting friendships with a couple of the other members, including the very congenial Joan.

I had limited social activities outside of church. Most of the close friends that I had attended high school with, including Melody and Mitzy, had left for the US to study and explore career opportunities that were not readily available in Jamaica. I kept in touch with a few of my batchmates from college by telephone, but hardly ever saw any of them, except for Karen.

Despite leading an active life, there was still a deficit in the love zone. Unlike other 'nubile bachelorettes' my age, I was not dating anyone.

One young man did all he could to engage my interest. He walked miles to visit me. To prove his love for me, he arrived at my house early one Saturday morning to help with my chores. Another loved the way I always made him laugh. He also thought it was a signal that I was ready for the attention of the opposite sex when I gave up wearing my long skirts for my new body-hugging Shelly-Ann jeans. It was just a coincidence that my church had recently relaxed the guideline on acceptable attire for their female members.

My guy friends were all very likeable young gentlemen, but to tell you the truth, I was trying to avoid romantic tragedy in my life. Instinctively I knew that Jay would never hurt me. I was content to continue holding out for him, even if it would take a little time for him to come back to me. I was sure that if Jay and I were ever together, my life with him would be close to perfect. But would Jay ever be here for me? Or would I have to find love with someone else?

7

A Glorious Promise

I RECEIVED MY ANSWER ABOUT FINDING love soon enough, when I met my new suitor. He would help me to take my mind off Jay.

My first job was as a kindergarten teacher. It was a one-year temporary post to replace a member of staff who had gone on study leave and would be returning for her job the following September. But I only found out my appointment was temporary as the end of the last term approached.

"But Miss Wallenston, you should have been told that the position was temporary," the newly appointed principal said indifferently.

"A year to be exact," she continued, "and that ends in June."

Her announcement came like a chilly wind on a sweltering summer day. Apparently, there were some struggles between the school board and the previous principal who had hired me. The miscommunication of my hiring terms had resulted in 'collateral damage' to my job.

At first, I was depressed and some of my colleagues were upset about the way the news was delivered. They called a meeting on my behalf to challenge the school. But I did not want any trouble, so I left quietly. Though I had enjoyed teaching kindergarten, I realized that I really wanted to be in the business world. I decided that I would teach part-time later in life – at the tertiary level, after equipping myself with higher qualifications and business experience.

I went job hunting.

Ms Bent, my mom's friend, told me of a temporary opening at her company for a clerical officer. I was looking for a job with some 'buzz', and one that would use my organizing skills, but I decided to take this job until something more suitable and permanent came up.

This was where I met Brad.

I was busy settling in at my desk on my first morning when he saw me. I saw him from the corner of my left eye as he strode over, oozing confidence. He was well-groomed and of average height, but his toned body bore an infantry-like posture to make up for what he lacked in height. He had a slim face with a straight nose and beady, but friendly eyes.

"Hello," he said, as he arrived at my desk. "I'm Brad Findlay. You are?"

His eyes landed on the more pronounced dimple in my left cheek. It was just a simple greeting, but I knew that he wanted to know more about me. The other managers had just walked by me with a nod and a quick "Good morning."

"Hi," I said. "I'm Wallenston, Sanaa Wallenston."

I wanted to sound formal, so I tried the James Bond introduction style. I did not want to say too much to encourage a conversation with him. I was not going to be around for long.

"Where did you work before you came here?" Brad asked. Then he quickly added, "Or is this your first job?"

I did not feel like answering that question. Why was he being so unnecessarily friendly? Why not stop at "Hi . . ." or maybe even ask how I was settling in?

"I was a teacher," I said, moving around the stationery on my desk.

"I have a sister who's a teacher," Brad responded quickly, happy to find something that could link us.

Oh boy, I thought, now he is going to want to know what I taught, where I taught and maybe even why I'm not teaching now.

But I was saved from the interrogation when his secretary stuck her head out of her office to tell him there was a telephone call holding for him. Brad paused, excused himself and muttered something over his shoulder about catching up with me tomorrow.

I resumed sorting out my desk after our brief introduction, wondering what Brad and I would speak about tomorrow.

Brad kept his word and came back to continue our conversation during the lunch period the following day. He was a well-educated, professionally trained career guy, an engineer. This was not surprising, given his position in the company. He was way above me in rank and should have been off-limits – but we chatted everyday thereafter, despite the speculations – the '*suss*' among office personnel about our involvement.

It was not instant attraction for me but I was growing to like Brad. He was not like the other guys I knew through my affiliation with the church. He was . . . worldly. This made me want to know more about him. He invited me out a couple of weeks after we met, but I was not sure if it was wise to take our association beyond the workmate level. But, he was persistent and after about two months of meeting, we went out.

Brad picked me up in his VW car, its noisy engine announcing that he was exactly on time for 7pm as we had agreed. He wanted to make sure I would be ready on his arrival and he had called when he was about to leave his home, which was a few minutes' drive from where I lived. I went out to meet him as it was still early for family introductions. I wore a pair of canary-yellow cropped pants with a white, eyelet cotton top. White high-heeled slides topped off my outfit.

"Wow", Brad said, "Yuh looking very nice Sanaa!" His eyes sparkled when he saw me, mirroring his appreciation for my outfit.

"You're looking quite relaxed, yourself, Brad."

We headed to the Devon House Grog Shoppe – my choice. The conversation was captivating and for the entire night I was wrapped up in Brad's tales about growing up in a rural area on the northeast side of Jamaica.

"Me and Theo, my younger brother used to get into a lot of scrapes away from home, but my old man always heard about our mischief and would whip us whether or not he got the story right," he chuckled. "Like the time me, Theo and another boy from up the road decided to hop on our neighbour, Mr Baker's dump truck to get a ride, rather than walking the three miles from school as it was about to rain. We spotted the truck just as he was about to pull out of a construction site across from our school yard. It was Theo's brilliant idea to seize this opportunity, assuming the truck was heading straight home. When we reached the junction leading to our district, Mr Baker hit the brake suddenly then turned left instead of going right for home!"

Brad paused, shaking his head with amusement as he remembered the afternoon. He continued,

"Before we realized what was happening, Theo's grip loosened and the next thing I saw was him sprawled in the middle of the junction, clutching his ankle while we were still hanging onto the truck. Me and the other boy jumped off the truck, scared we would break our legs as the truck was picking up speed. Apparently, Mr Baker had plans to go into town for construction supplies that afternoon! Luckily, Theo didn't break his ankle, but we had to cradle him between our joined arms and half-carry him home while he hopped on his good leg."

"So, what happened when yuh got home?"

I leaned in, as I asked, anxious to know their fate.

"Well, the usual," Brad said.

"Mama rushed out to see what was happening when she heard Theo bawling. And Maas Rupert was not home yet, but Mama gave him her version of the story we told her. I got my whipping and Theo got an even worse one for almost breaking his leg."

We were both laughing hard, though I was feeling sorry for Theo, who I had not yet met.

"Then to add embarrassment to near injury, next morning before we left for school, my father, being the exemplary member of the district that he was, made us apologize to Mr Baker for hopping onto his truck."

"What did Mr Baker say?"

"He didn't know about that particular incident; boys hopped onto his truck every day . . . but he accepted our apology."

I was very happy to have some country episodes of my own to share with Brad, though they were probably not as exciting as his were. But I still felt my experience with country life helped to put us on common ground. Apart from that, there were not many similarities between our youthful lives. Unlike me, Brad was from a two-parent home. He had a good relationship with both his parents now and visited them in the country almost weekly. His parents were Christians, but he said he was leaning towards being agnostic. Though a Christian myself, I understood his questioning of some God-related matters.

Brad had studied overseas and now he had a good job. But he led a moderate rather than elaborate lifestyle, despite his attainments. There was no mention of any immediate plans regarding what he wanted for his future.

The nearly three hours hanging out was pleasant but I did not expect anything more than friendship, especially since he had shared that he was in the middle of a breakup. As we got up to leave, Brad said,

"This was a really nice evening Sanaa. Yuh sure you ready to end it?"

I laughed ... not sure what he expected me to say.

"We could go to your house or mine," he said with a chuckle.

I realized that Brad was serious and wanted to spend some more time with me; after all, it was on the long weekend leading to National Heroes Day and just 10pm – still early. But I could not invite him to my house at that time.

He was his own man – though he shared a house with his two older sisters.

"I could stop by your place since it's on the way home," I said tentatively. But I can't stay long – it's just to see where yuh live."

Brad looked pleased.

"OK!" he said.

We had light conversation about work and other topical matters as we made our way to his house. When we got there, Brad showed me his side of the house. I made a mental note of the fact that there was still some tell-tale evidence of his sweetheart spending time there. Had they really broken up?

"Brad, I need to go now," I said.

It had been a bad idea to stop at his place. I had to get home before Mom started worrying, anyway.

We left.

Soon, Brad was pulling up to my gate.

"Thank you for a lovely evening Brad … good night," I said reaching to open the car door, not wanting to linger.

I let myself out of the car. Brad ran to my side before I could leave.

"Sanaa … there's just one more thing before you go …"

Brad was now standing between me and my gate. I felt his hands on my back pulling me into him.

"I've wanted to do this all evening," he whispered, and in the same breath, his head swooped down, and he was kissing me – his tongue searching the softness of my lips, slightly parted from surprise. I was flustered and tried to back up but did not get far as he was still loosely holding me.

Here I was, thinking I was an enlightened woman, ready for romance, yet I had no knowledge about men and dating.

Jay and I had only shared hugs and quick pecks on the lips when we saw each other. I had never even been on a real date, and certainly not with a man of the world who would naturally expect physical intimacy with a woman he desired.

"Let's take a step back," I said to him after his attempted kiss.

"A step back?" he queried, looking puzzled.

"I mean . . . let's slow down," I said. "Just until yuh sure you're free – really free to date me as I don't plan to share yuh."

Brad smiled and nodded. Then he gave me a quick peck on the cheek and said, "Good night Sanaa."

At the office, Brad continued coming by my desk every chance he got. The rapport kept my curiosity about him warm. A few weeks after we had gone out he also convinced me his old relationship was over. Then, in the New Year – three months after our first evening out, we went on an official date.

Before I realized what was happening, my curiosity with Brad grew into something I had never experienced before – a heady ardour. I wanted to know if this thing was love on Brad's part or if it was just a physical attraction. A mere touch from him made me feel tingly all over and I was sure that I was falling in love. I wanted to be in love and I wanted him to love me back. What would I do if he did not? My desire for love defied innate logic, as I still felt we were from different worlds. Yet, Brad seemed flawless in my estimation.

This was a wonderfully exciting time in my life. It had to be love.

Everyone close to me, including Jay who was still overseas, knew I had met a guy who I liked a lot. I blushed constantly when I spoke about Brad and even now, I can still remember how the intensity of my feelings for him grew rapidly as we got to know each other. I could not eat, could not sleep and for a while I could not allow myself to think about Jay. I listened keenly to Naomi's advice on love. She was happy for me: but she cautioned me to take things slowly.

"Sanaa, no matter how yuh feel, don't lower yuh standards, girl."

Tony felt triumphant; his ice-queen sister was burning up with love. Both he and our last boarder-turned-family-member, Raquel, would race to answer the telephone every evening at about 6pm when Brad would call me. Even my mom positioned herself one evening to answer the telephone to hear him. There was something different about this guy! I did not freeze him out as I did the others and she figured he was shaping up to be more than just a friend. Why had she not yet met him? She probed:

"Sanaa, who is this Mr Brad what's-his-name? What is he about?"

"He's just a guy I met at work, very interesting," I said.

She probed further wanting to know more about this new guy who had my interest.

"Is this Brad a Christian?"

"No, Mommy, but he is decent."

"Be careful yuh nuh Sanaa," Mom warned, "I don't want any crying in here. Just make sure he comes in to meet me next time he's here to pick yuh up."

There ended the inevitable interrogation about Brad from the sole parent I had who cared about me. Having filled her in on Brad, I assured my mom that I was the same daughter I had always been. And so, my family accepted that I had a real boyfriend. I beamed every day at work, and at home sang at the top of my voice along with groups like Air Supply about the excitement of love. Tony and Raquel would join in as back-up singers – all of us laughing out loud when we could not hit, much less hold the high notes of these songs that seemed to last an infinity. My romantic mood was infectious.

My Mom met Brad the next time he came to pick me up for a date. We were going to see a play. I took him straight into her bedroom where she was sewing.

"Mommy, this is Brad," I said proudly.

"Hello Brad," Mom said.

"Good night, Ms Mullings," Brad responded.

She did not get up from her sewing machine, but paused from stitching when he extended his arm to shake her hand.

"So, I hear your father is a farmer and a tailor."

"Yes," Brad said. ". . . He gave up the sewing a few years ago, but this scene is very familiar to me. This is the same way he would be working late into the evenings around his machine," Brad chuckled.

"Two things we were sure of while growing up is that Maas Rupert would always work around the clock and keep us straight with some beatings."

We all laughed and it seemed the perfect note on which to leave for the date – but not before Mom grilled him a bit about his job, though I had already told her what he did.

"Well it was nice meeting you, Ms Mullings," Brad said after a few more minutes with Mom. I will see you again soon."

"Ok, Brad. It was nice to meet you too. You are welcome to come in anytime." Mom was speaking her best English – a sure sign she liked my boyfriend.

His display of charm won her over, though she had expressed concern that he was not in the church, given my own Christian commitment.

After Brad met my mother, our dating increased.

Sometimes we would go to drive-in movies after work. On weekends, we drove around the city and ate pan chicken.

He had a knack for listening to my endless musings about what I wanted to do with my future and I loved him for this. He was almost always with me when he was not working late and that was reassuring. For the first time, I felt that I was in love with someone who was available to love me back.

That Christmas, Jay's mother visited Jamaica and we spent some time together. She invited me out to see a play.

I guess she was impressed with me, as Jay related that

when she returned home, she kept extolling my virtues. She felt that he was wasting time where I was concerned, and he agreed.

Talk about bad timing.

The truth is, I still loved Jay and he admitted to loving me. But the distance between us had prevented us from nurturing our love. Now I was trying to move forward with Brad. And why not? My feelings for him were gobbling me up. But our fledgling relationship was now being challenged – from all sides.

Brad's ex-girlfriend was not ready to give him up. He said nothing was happening between them – they were just old friends now. I was not sure about the extent of their friendship as they were spending a lot of time together while he did this or that for her.

At the start of the New Year, I decided to cool off from dating and the complications it brought. I now had a new job in the airline industry that would allow me to experience the wider world, as I had been hoping. I was based at the airport in Kingston, an exciting working environment, where apart from safety and standard operating procedures, no two days were the same. My new job would help me to take my mind off Brad for a while.

"Brad," I advised him, "I'll need to focus on the training for my new job for the next three weeks."

But I really needed the time to decide if we should continue our relationship. It would certainly help that I was no longer working around him daily. After a few weeks,

Brad called me. He had something he had to tell me and wanted us to meet.

"Sanaa," Brad said, his voice almost trembling. "I don't know about you, but I can't stand when we're apart."

I was ecstatic. This is what I had been waiting to hear – that Brad wanted to be with me as much as I wanted to be with him.

We went out for drinks after work the following Friday evening.

"Bwoy, Sanaa, this time-out thing wasn't working for me," Brad said as he held both my hands.

"I missed yuh so much; I hope this means we are back together."

"I know," I said. "Because it's the same for me."

With that, Brad and I were back together. We had passed the first test of our love and I had his undivided attention once again. I was happy to be back in his arms. I thought of nothing else but the feeling of being in love. It was potent as a drug – transporting me to heights I had never known before meeting Brad Findlay. Every day at work and at home, I spoke glowingly of my beau. I was in love and wanted everyone to know.

We started spending even more quality time together. Often, on weekends, we took one-day trips out of town, stopping to visit places of interest along the island's coast. Our discussions were often about Jamaican politics and anything else that was topical. Both of our families were traditional supporters of the PNP but being of Jamaica's post-socialism generation, Brad and I were probably far more aware of the impact of politics on our nation than our parents were. He spoke with such passion about politics that I often wondered if he had a secret ambition to run for political office! His mode of governance would not have been popular though, as he had drastic ideas about how the government should deal with hindrances to national progress, like corruption and crime – two growing phenomena that the authorities seemed incapable of controlling.

To get more insight into Brad's political views (and to impress him), I read a few books on politics from his personal library, which unsurprisingly included Michael Manley's *Politics of Change,* which focused on equality and social justice. But I was quite surprised to find among his collection a very thick volume of *Mein Kampf,* a winding, chilling autobiographical treatise on Adolf Hitler's political philosophy.

"How come yuh have this book?" I asked Brad having read the blurb and flipped through its contents.

"Oh . . . that . . ." Brad seemed to have forgotten he had it.

"It was part of my required reading at university," he said.

That was it; he offered no commentary on the book – or warning of its content.

After reading Brad's book, I understood that the way the world works was driven by ideologies and, in this case, when implemented, it was extreme and detrimental.

As I got closer to Brad I felt a sense of belonging with him. My emotional walls came down and I got past my intimacy inhibitions. After an extended dating period I converted into a very sensual woman as he turned up the romance!

What more could I have asked for?

Yet, something told me that this new emotion I was thriving on was too intense to be safe. How would I cope if Brad suddenly took all this attention from me? I wanted to pull back, but it was too late. I had fallen insanely in love with Brad and I was naïve enough to believe that he was falling in love with me at the same pace.

As we progressed into our relationship, I found out that being Brad's girlfriend came with many conditions. That was not so thrilling. His expectations were that he would make my decisions, approve or disapprove of my activities and always, always have tabs on my location. My free time should be spent with him, at home, or somewhere that he could account for me. Yet, this did not guarantee his commitment to me.

I soon discovered that I was more in love with Brad than he was with me. The love train was moving too fast for him. Or, perhaps, he was just maladroit at handling matters of the heart. Perhaps he did not know how to allow himself to enjoy true love. He was avoiding any activity that involved our friends and families, which would imply a serious commitment between us. He had involved his ex-girlfriend in his family life and it had not worked out well.

We were making no plans for a future together.

"Brad, how many kids would yuh like when yuh get married?" I had asked more than once.

His answer was consistent.

"Married? Children? Not sure about any of that yet babes." Brad was clearly uncomfortable with any discussions about the future.

The question of whether we would get married in the future, however, was the least of my dilemma with Brad at that time. Nearly two years of steady dating is not such a long time when you are young. There was still time for planning our future and our life of adventure together, if things worked out. After all, I had more immediate personal goals, such as pursuing higher studies.

What puzzled me most about Brad was his unveiling of a steely side of himself, which was the direct opposite of the charming, thoughtful individual that I had met and to whom I had given myself.

He no longer called me throughout the daytime to enquire if my day was going well. The calls only came to check if I was at home by a certain time. No more listening to my dreams, they were too unconventional for him and too far beyond the present. Why not live one day at a time?

I did not want to believe that one man could be so different from his former self. It was like being swept-up and spun in an enchanting waltz by a man behind a mask at a masquerade party. Now, the music was fading, and I was begining to wake up from my dream of having found true love. We started drifting apart and, while cautiously coming down from the steep side of this unravelling love, tragedy struck.

Jay and I had continued writing to each other even after I told him about Brad. He thought it was good for me to have a companion, so, when I came home one evening and got yet another letter from Canada, it was not out of the ordinary – except for the handwriting.

I tore open the letter – but gingerly, not sure what to expect. The letter was from Jay, but his sister had written it.

Jay was gravely ill.

"Jay has leukaemia," she wrote, "and it has progressed rapidly."

The words on the paper were painful to read and hard to believe.

At only 25 years old, Jay was terminally ill!

I was devastated, heartbroken. How could God allow this to happen to a child of His? Jay was so bright, so promising. Having completed a first degree in sociology, he was studying to become a lawyer and had hoped to return home to help make his country of birth, his beloved 'Rock', a more just society with his passion for human rights and for helping the disempowered.

Jay had often invited me to visit him in the "Great White North" (as he often referred to Canada). Now in this time of need, he urged me to come and see him. My boss wrote a compelling letter to the Canadian High Commission, but I did not get the required visa to visit Jay at this critical time of his life.

After a few months of beginning his treatment and seeing signs of remission, Jay visited Jamaica during Easter. His plan was to take a trip around the island. I did not anticipate that he would want me to go on this trip with him.

Unsure about my relationship status with Brad, I decided against going on the trip with Jay. Brad would not have understood my motivation for going out of town with another man – terminally ill or not – even though our relationship was sliding. Jay did not question me about this decision – he just accepted it and went on his trip by himself. I felt bad for letting him go alone. What would I do if something happened to him out there? But, Jay was always fearless. He did not focus on his illness.

"With God, everything is under control," he often reminded me.

After he returned from his solo expedition, we spent some time together. We went to a football match between Canada and Jamaica and of course, stopped by my favourite place, Devon House, known for its open spaces, peaceful atmosphere and architectural remnants of nineteenth-century post-colonial gentry. I felt it was exactly what Jay needed.

The mansion's outstanding Georgian design may seem like a misfit in the centre of Kingston, but for me it reflects the city's haute history, its mystique subtly blending into our modern-day lifestyle; offering respite from everyday predicaments, like the one Jay now faced.

Jay and I held hands and walked along its gardens. The hours quickly slipped away as we were oblivious of others around us, talking about what we could do at our level to make Jamaica a better place.

"Sanaa, I can't get over how beautiful Jamaica is every time I'm here," Jay said.

"It is such a pity that so many persons have to struggle and work so hard yet can't really have a good life."

"Well," I said. "Yuh have to remember we are a young nation emerging from slavery and a system of vast inequality."

"Yes," Jay responded. "And that is why we vote in politicians every five years . . . so that we can see some real progress. But things don't look too different from when I left here in the '70s. I'm not saying there is no change . . . just not enough."

"So, what needs to happen, Jay?" I asked.

"The social systems, especially education, have to work better … so that 99 percent of youths coming out of secondary schools are literate and have a skill – even if they can't afford university. Too many people leaving school and don't have the skills to work."

That was his main concern.

We ended the afternoon dining leisurely at the mansion's Grog Shoppe, which boasts a tasty selection of traditional Jamaican cuisine and signature cocktails like *Devon House Duppy*. Later in the evening, Jay introduced me to his (paternal) grandmother and some other relatives. They were all excited to meet me and I especially liked his grandmother, who was rather witty, though well on in years.

On Jay's last day in Jamaica, I took the day off from work. I went to see him at his maternal grandmother's home where he always stayed when visiting. The time went quickly and soon it was time for me to head home. Jay decided to take me home despite the risk of him missing his flight.

Instead of leaving me at my gate, he followed me into the house. He was acting as if there was something he had to do that was even more important than catching his flight to Toronto. Mom was off on one of her downtown excursions and Uncle Herbert was dozing on the verandah.

Jay stopped in the middle of our living room and turned to me. He had an earnest yet gentle look in his eyes, which now seemed even darker than they used to be, because of the pallor of his skin.

"Sanaa," he said taking my hands, "can't you feel it?"

My heart was racing but I tried to appear cool, not sure if he was feeling the same thing I was feeling.

"Feel what?" I asked.

Jay smiled his beautiful lopsided smile. Even with his

head now bald from chemotherapy, his handsomeness was disarming.

"We shouldn't continue to deny the love between us. Let's get married as soon as I have conquered this disease."

I was stunned.

I threw my arms around Jay's neck and we hugged, squeezing each other. But the reality that his illness could cut his life short, quickly ousted the joy that had welled up in me.

I stepped back from Jay. He had remained a positive person despite his illness – but to propose marriage at a time like this?

"Remember I've been seeing someone," I muttered.

"Sanaa, what do you really have with Brad? Is that what you really want?"

Jay knew me well. He could see right into my heart and knew what I was feeling for him. He wanted me to commit to him there and then.

"I'm trusting you to make the right decision, Sanaa, to wait on me to recover and get back on my feet and on with my life . . . our life."

Then Jay reminded me that he was departing the island that same day and he wanted to leave with his answer intact. This should have been easy enough, but it was not.

There were too many emotions to face and too many decisions to make, in too short a time.

I sobbed uncontrollably while I again hugged Jay, wishing I never had to let him go.

"Sanaa, why are you crying?" Jay asked, gently wiping away my tears.

I hated that he sounded like the strong one, when he was the one with his life hanging on a thread, so fragile and uncertain.

"I'm afraid I won't see you again," I whispered.

"But you will, Sanaa. I won't give up," he smiled reassuringly.

Before we parted, Jay gently cupped my face in his hands and kissed me, and his kiss spoke of his love for me and the life that he needed to hold on to – for hope in our future.

Then he asked, "Sanaa, will you wait for me?"

And I said, "Yes."

What else could I have said?

Jay and I had one last kiss and then I walked him back to the car.

I watched him drive away, tears stinging my face as I realized that time now held the secret of our destiny.

Jay's proposal seemed surreal. I never really allowed myself to relish what had happened in the middle of my living room after he left. When I told Raquel about Jay's proposal, she was excited; but she understood that this was not a straightforward situation.

That night and many nights thereafter I prayed for Jay's recovery. Before falling asleep I would feel assured of his healing. But often I was awoken in the middle of the night from a haunting dream in which there was one man with two faces: Brad's and Jay's. I had no idea that I would have been the leading lady in such a scene. Jay was the last person I could ever hurt. I was trying to do the right thing – trying not to hurt anyone. To make matters worse, Brad was working to patch things up with me, using tenderness as his leverage. He knew how close Jay and I were and how much Jay's illness had affected me.

At that point, I was not sure how to deal with my feelings for Brad, but I needed someone to lean on. So, I kept everything that had transpired between Jay and me from Brad. I did not want him to think that I was being unfaithful to him, since whatever affection we shared had not fully expired. I just did not know what to do in this love triad. Can one woman love two men at the same time? Yes. I did. But their love seemed elusive.

Jay did not make it. His last letter to me was in August, that same year. After receiving this letter, written in his handwriting distorted by pain and feebleness, I called him. His voice was vacant. It lacked his trademark optimism, sounding a knell that if I did not see him soon, I would never see him again. There was not much conversation, but the silence between our words was heavy with sadness. Jay needed to get some rest. I hung up and then I cried uncontrollably, tormented because I could do nothing to help him. I could not even hold him.

This was our last conversation.

Jay passed one week later, in early September.

When the news came, I was hysterical. How would I live without my best friend, my confidant, my future mate? Jay had left me forever. No proper goodbye was said. It was an unfitting end to our very special bond.

My chance for bidding my soulmate goodbye came when I was able to travel to Canada the following year. I stayed with Jay's parents in their home. I slept in his sunken bed in which he had spent so much of his last days, racked by pain. Jay's family took me to visit his grave and I spoke to him there for the last time. This gave me a chance to better handle my grief. I could begin to get closure –begin to fully appreciate the rather colorful chapter Jay had added to my life.

8

The Abyss of Bittersweet Love

IN THE AFTERMATH OF JAY'S DEATH, Hurricane Gilbert hit the island on September 12, 1988. It exacerbated my still raw sadness. This was one of Jamaica's worst hurricanes. I certainly had never seen such a storm in my lifetime.

It was a Sunday and I was at work when I heard the hurricane warnings. I thought nothing of this as, every year, we had a hurricane season that lasted for six months, with lots of named storms and hurricanes developing, but no direct hit. They would dissipate with maybe some heavy rains and, at most, flooding in low-lying areas. However, Gilbert was gaining strength.

As soon as the flight departed, my office mates and I hurried from the partially deserted airport. We exercised great caution, scurrying out of harm's way to leave the road that led from the airport to Kingston; only a narrow strip of land separated us from the very seas on which Gilbert was travelling towards us. Any storm surge would have cut us off from the mainland. We had no way of knowing that by the following evening Gilbert would come ashore, landing as a ferocious category three hurricane, pounding impatiently on our doors.

We started battening down at home the next morning, but it was already too late. In a frenzy, we nailed here, chopped fruit trees there, while sporadic, squally showers came at us like darts from the sky, a prelude to Gilbert's full attack. Before long, the rains forced us to retreat inside the house. We did not get a chance to pare the Bombay mango tree and when Gilbert passed over us later that night, bringing gale force winds and torrential rains, one of its limbs came crashing down, right where my bedroom was located. The front awning took the brunt of the damage.

The kitchen roof did not fare so well. Gilbert's howling winds lifted one of its corners and the rains came tumbling in. We – Mommy, Raquel, Tony, Gary's two kids, Uncle Herbert, one of Brenda's sisters and her kids and I – were all huddled together in the living room, when we heard the roof rumbling as it started to lift. We felt a sudden gust of air filling the house, putting out the light from the candles, leaving only the flicker from our Home Sweet Home lamp, which dipped but somehow withstood the draught.

Frenetically, with only a "Lawd Jesus", Mom jumped up and scrambled in the direction of the kitchen. No instructions needed. Tony, Raquel and I disbanded to the corners of the kitchen, trying desperately to get rid of the intruding water using wet mop, dry mop, towels and newspapers. We used whatever we could find to absorb the rain coming into the house – fearful of a watery death.

Throughout the remainder of the night, we faced-off with Gilbert from our kitchen, while sending up supplications to the Almighty for the long, dark, frightening night to end. The entire area had already lost electricity. The lashing of the winds and the heavy rains lasted for most of the night, and we were relieved when daylight broke through the heavy sheath of darkness to erase its terror. Trepidation took over from relief as we peeped out to view our yard, stripped almost bare by Gilbert's onslaught. I wondered if this picture was a sign of what Gilbert had done to the rest of the island.

Two days after Gilbert passed, I ventured out of my yard to see what damage the hurricane had done in the neighbourhood. There was desolation as far as I could see. Reports from the radio stations were that the hurricane had left a trail of destruction across Jamaica. Several homes and other buildings had lost their entire roofs, and others had been mercilessly demolished. We felt lucky. Ours was one of the houses that had experienced only minor damage. We lost only our pear and cherry trees.

It seemed like in less than 24 hours, Jamaica had gone from being an idyllic and beautiful island to a denuded one. Saddest was that 45 persons lost their lives, all because of "Wild Gilbert", as the hurricane was later referred to in a popular song. Social and essential services were all in disarray after Gilbert passed, leaving many homes without electricity and piped water for months. The destruction of the many farms in the rural areas led to severe food shortages for a very long time after that hurricane. Sale of canned foods soared.

One of the most vivid images created by the disaster was that of a small aircraft trapped between the limbs of a tree along the corridor leading to the airport. It had not been secured in a hangar and the storm hoisted and landed it in the tree. Anyone who had to go to the Norman Manley International Airport in Kingston after Gilbert would have seen it. It remained there for years, as a reminder of the destruction that Gilbert had wreaked.

Shortly after the hurricane, Brad went on an extensive work trip to an eastern Caribbean island. For months, there was no word from him. I contacted his sister twice inquiring about him and she said he was OK.

After almost half a year, Brad returned home, assuming he could resume our relationship.

"Hi Sanaa . . . I can't wait to see yuh," Brad announced on his first call to me.

"I'm glad you're back too . . . but how come I never heard from yuh all these months?" I queried, giving him no chance to answer.

"Brad, I'm really tired of how yuh treat me . . . out of sight, out of mind."

"I'll talk to yuh tomorrow."

I hung up the phone.

Brad rang back immediately.

"Sanaa . . . come on! Yuh didn't hear that that bad hurricane made calling out impossible from the eastern islands?"

I did not answer for a while. We both knew that what he offered was no real excuse. He could have written to me; or at least sent a card.

Brad continued talking and I listened.

His lack of sensitivity infuriated me.

After a few weeks and a few more calls from Brad, I decided to give the relationship another chance. As we say in Jamaica, "Ole fire-stick easy fi ketch."

Brad was the only modicum of love I had left, so I slowly let go of my wariness of him and started to grow, once again, confident in our future together.

The following year, I started university to further my education. Life became hectic as I continued working full-time, but I still made time for Brad.

In the wider arena, news from around the world was that communism was toppling – led by a man called Mikhail Gorbachev from the Soviet Union. And there was a briskness in the air in Jamaica too, when this new wave of political change emerged. The changes were indeed sweeping as over in East Germany, the Berlin Wall, a strong symbol of communism and the last bastion of the Cold

War, could not withstand the pressures of Gorbachev's call for *'Glasnost'* and *'Perestroika'* for openness and restructuring of the global political system. The wall came tumbling down in November 1989.

In 1990, Gorbachev was awarded the Noble Peace Prize for effectively leading the end of the Cold War, without any nuclear catastrophe. A New World Order was surfacing – a new political thinking that promoted tolerance and cooperation between sovereign nations. This paved the way for globalization, supported by technological advancements.

When Michael Manley showed that his brand of politics had also changed from radical to a more moderate socialism, in tune with the global changes, the political cards stacked up in his favour. Although Edward Seaga had tried to follow through with his promise to restore the country to a free market economy, he had not scored a high enough grade in his attempt to reduce poverty – to "mek money jingle" in our pockets, as he had promised in 1980. He had advocated 'belt tightening' as a way of stimulating economic growth, but the people who had clamoured for his leadership before 1980 couldn't handle the restrictions imposed on them. They voted him out of office. According to one of my favourite political science lecturers at university, in the 1989 election, the Jamaican electorate voted for 'bread and butter issues', not ideology.

I was happy to witness the positive changes in a world no longer divided by political fences. And I was happy that the political tension in Jamaica had eased over the years. But in my own life, a new wave of distrust was tearing down my once blind faith in Brad, and it was tumbling just like the Berlin Wall.

I was purposefully focusing on my studies and trying to maintain a balanced life, when I found out that Brad was straying from me. An associate at work, who happened to have a boyfriend working in a subsidiary of Brad's organization, gave me this news while we were having lunch with another colleague. We were having a general conversation about relationship challenges and this was her opportunity to break some related news.

"Sanaa, yuh and Brad still together?"

I paused. Why would she blatantly ask such a personal question in front of another co-worker – especially given the conversation we were having? The other co-worker, whom I was closer to, fell silent.

"What yuh mean," I asked – buying time to respond.

"Well, my boyfriend said Brad is seeing someone – a girl who works at his office," she said.

I bristled.

"Well, if they work in the same place they must see each other," I said, pretending to be obtuse.

She persisted.

"I don't know what yuh call it if him go home with her in the evenings."

I guess she did not think she could convince me without being brutal.

Then she excused herself from the table.

How could I believe this report? Brad? Not too long ago he had begged me to take him back after missing me for months.

The conversation stayed on my mind through to the next day, while my co-worker and I avoided each other. I was as embarrassed as I was emotionally worn out by Brad's games. He was being non-committal in our relationship – with one foot in and one foot out, as if he were playing hopscotch on my heart. Yet I did not know how to break the spell between us. I decided to ignore my informant, choosing to believe instead that her report was just a nasty rumour.

This is the period of my life I am least proud of – I was living a paradox.

There I was, a (supposedly) progressive young woman, determined to further my studies to improve my career path and my life. Yet, I was not standing up for my own principles and convictions. I was trying to please everyone and I was taking whatever little Brad chose to offer me. I had even convinced myself that Brad loved me. Well, this was until I witnessed his modus operandus first-hand.

When I started attending university, Brad had asked me for my timetable and I had given it to him, thinking that he was showing interest in my studies. His intentions came to light not too long after my troublesome co-worker had warned me.

I was on campus late one afternoon, walking through the Faculty of Arts courtyard, when I glimpsed the unmistakable colour and outline of Brad's vintage car. It was chugging its way down Ring Road, the university's central thoroughfare.

"Had he come looking for me?" I thought to myself.

But, I should not have been on campus at that time. I had only gone there to hand in an assignment. As I peered ahead more intently, I saw that some other damsel was being shuttled away in my boyfriend's car! Flabbergasted, I stalled for a moment, befuddled and upset. I was not sure what to make of what I had seen. Quickly, I took the direct route leading from the courtyard to the university's front gate, hoping to get a closer look at the evidence of Brad's betrayal of my trust exiting the campus. But, they had already sped away by the time I got there.

Like a somnambulist, I made my way through the front gate and across to the bus stop to get my bus to Half-Way-Tree. It was overcast and getting late and I needed to get home. I needed to get away as fast as I could from the scene of treachery.

As I stood waiting for my bus, it started raining heavily, but the showers could not wash away the scene I had left behind. Neither could my flimsy umbrella shield me from the brunt of the rain as I tried to fit under the narrow open bus shed with the other waiting commuters. The scene from the last few minutes on the campus was playing over and over in my mind – only allowing for unanswered questions and damning my trust in Brad.

Generally, I relied on public transportation to get

around. There were days when I had to go on the university campus twice – morning and evening, and to work in between. Travelling between these far-flung points on any given day was no easy feat – it required careful logistics planning. Some mornings when I had early classes, I would be lucky to get a ride to school with Karen, who lived in an adjoining neighbourhood, less than 10 minutes from my house. Otherwise, it was just the unreliable public bus service for daily transport (save for those times when a kind motorist going in my direction offered me a ride).

The buses plying the route to the university were few; you could wait for hours at the bus stop before one came along. Often they already had full passenger loads originating from downtown.

The alternative was the tiny 12-seat minivans, with no standing room, which would carry 20 or more passengers per trip. These were my options for getting to school and work.

Brad would sometimes take me to the airport on a weekend when I had to work, but he had never offered to take me to school or back home in the evenings. It was incomprehensible to me why someone else was receiving this gallant treatment from him, while I had to find my own transportation.

When I got home, I went straight to Mom's bedroom and sat on the edge of her bed. She was sewing.

"Oh Lawd, I'm glad yuh didn't get soaked in the rain," Mom said on seeing me come into her room.

I was concentrating very hard on holding back my tears, while Mom rambled on,

"I got a letter from yuh Auntie Nell today."

I heard nothing else she was saying.

I wanted to tell her so badly about what I had seen and how it was cutting me up on the inside, but I knew that once I started talking I would start crying. I did not want my mother to see my tears, so I said goodnight and made an excuse about getting out of my damp clothes.

That night, I poured my heartache out onto paper. I had spent all these years with Brad and all I had become for loving him was an icon of pain.

For nearly one entire week after that rainy night, I cried into my pillow every night whenever I was alone. During the day, I had to pretend things were normal. I had to act perky at work because I did not want my co-workers to see my pain – especially not the over-exuberant whistle-blower. But nothing went unnoticed in that office.

We were a small staff of seven full-time persons and a few part-timers. We all knew what was going on in each other's lives; we knew who had happy relationships and marriages and we all knew whose significant others were not playing by the rules of love.

I scraped together what little pride I had left and admitted to myself that I did not enjoy the place in Brad's life that I thought I did. I could not endure being the other woman in his life. I felt I could not face him. When Brad finally contacted me days after the campus incident, he could not understand why I was frosty towards him. About two weeks after his attempt to talk with me, I worked up the courage to confront him about his actions. Of course, Brad denied that I had seen him picking up another woman on the campus that day.

"Brad," I said quite directly. "I know yuh seeing someone else from UWI."

His eyes bulged widely at my accusation.

"Why yuh say that?" Brad asked.

"Because I saw yuh there picking her up. Don't deny it."

He did not . . . not really.

"Yes", I had seen his vehicle there and "Yes", he knew the young lady who was picked up in it, but, "No", he was not the one driving; it was a colleague from his office who had used his car to pick up the mystery woman.

Brad tried to get off his indictment on a technicality. I had not proven anything. And the rumours persisted, much to my chagrin. When I finally revealed the source of my information to Brad, he gave in and explained that he had been seeing the lady in question.

"But babes, that don't mean that things have to be different between us."

"Yuh know that sometimes yuh moody." Brad went on, "I not sure if yuh really want me, to tell the truth, Sanaa."

I just stared at him. He was right; I could be moody and sometimes liked to have time to myself. But that was no reason for him to shift the blame for straying.

Brad muttered,

"But sorry, I didn't mean to hurt yuh. Yuh have mi ticket, yuh know that."

Why was I worried? Matter settled. Or was it? That was Brad's attempt to spare my feelings or, more plausibly, himself. For me the damage was irreparable.

I still had to deal with the churning feeling in the pit of my stomach each time I approached the university gates, nervous about running into my *matey*. There was no easy way around this problem. Lucky for me, I had applied for a transfer to the Faculty of Social Sciences before the semester ended and it came through for the next school year. It became a little easier to attend the same school with Brad's new love, as the breadth between the faculties separated us. I still saw her a few times for the remainder of my studies, but this was only when I used the main campus library.

My close friends knew of my conflicting feelings for Brad and I knew that they never quite understood what had kept me tied to him. I certainly did not. The only person who I dared to share this matter with, blow-by-blow, was Karen. I always felt comfortable sharing my innermost girly feelings for Brad with her, free from judgement.

I would tell Karen how much I loved Brad and wanted to be with him and she would understand and not expect me to be rational about it.

I was the same with her when she told me about the challenges in her marriage.

We often compared our love lives to see whose was more ludicrous.

I had to unburden this new development with Brad.

"Karen," I said, "remember when I told yuh that my colleague warned me Brad was seeing another woman?

"It's true." I said.

Karen looked surprised.

"Yuh sure?" she asked.

"Well, guess what; I saw it for myself on campus – long story – and now we're over," I said.

Karen paused knowingly.

"For how long Sanaa?" She hastily added in a firm yet understanding tone, "It not so easy to walk away from love, but sometimes we have to try if we are always hurting."

And I was hurting. So, I walked away from Brad, with intentions of never looking back. I was determined to get over him and had no plans to get involved with anyone else.

A few months after parting with Brad, I met Matthew.

My friend from work, the innocent party present at the lunch table when I found out about Brad's affair, introduced us. She insisted that he was quite different from Brad and after just one date with him, it was obvious that she was right. Matthew was a lot younger than Brad and had a different approach to dating. He reminded me of Jay – patient and with a strong sense of humour.

My first date with Matthew was awesome. We went to a *Soca* fete and it was the perfect choice because I loved dancing. One date led to several dates and I was convinced that he was good for me because he took my mind off my breakup with Brad Findlay.

Sometimes Matthew would pick me up from work, just to take me to school, even after he had had a hard day at work. It felt good having someone look out for me. We saw each other when we wanted to and that was a welcome change. We had a good time dating for a few months, but Matthew thought our relationship should have been progressing, faster.

After a delayed flight caused me to work late one evening, I called Matthew and asked him to come pick me up. We had not seen each other for a couple of weeks, so I was looking forward to seeing him. On the way home, we had some light but halting conversation about how his business was doing and what I had been up to during those past weeks. After a prolonged silence, Matthew respectfully asked,

"Sanaa, how much longer must I wait? When yuh going to take the next step with me?"

I had not expected this and did not know how to respond.

The truth was that the break-up with Brad had dampened my urge to be in another real relationship just months after we parted. I was being unfair to Matthew; the relationship could not go on as it had since we had started dating. It was like an airplane that had taxied down a runway but was just not able to take off.

There was no need for Matthew to say anything further. Whatever I had with him was over by the time he dropped me home.

That was when I realized that I had not gotten over Brad.

Since our official parting, Brad had kept in touch with me and still behaved jealous over my involvement with Matthew, who I had told him about. To him, it was a sure sign I had moved on, but I was not sure he accepted it.

As soon as Matthew was out of the picture, Brad was right there to court me all over again, crooning regret and promising better behaviour for our next round of love.

"Brad, last time I checked yuh had a girlfriend, remember?"

"Sanaa, me and that lady just couldn't make it. It's over; she just wasn't right for me. I swear . . . you are the one for me."

You would think that my latest entanglement with Brad would have been my last with him, but somewhere in the land of sad love stories, our names were deeply inscribed.

Had I forgotten that when Brad was in my life, he was my constant source of angst because he only played with my heart?

Had I forgotten how much he had hurt me, and publicly?

Or had I forgotten that what I wanted was far more than what Brad was prepared to offer me?

I gave Brad's argument some thought, before giving in, but it was not an easy make up. He had seriously damaged my trust in him, and I prayed that he was ready to give our relationship the chance it deserved.

By now I was living on my own. Brad started spending more time with me at my place. He enjoyed my cooking and I liked when he was there watching TV or reading while I studied. I gave him a key to my apartment. It was my way of symbolizing that I had forgiven him. After all, he was the closest person I could call on when Tony was not around.

You may think it was irrational for me to reunite with Brad, again. During our off-periods, I would only remember his charm and special knack for comforting me when things went wrong in other areas of my life. Yet, when we were on, it often felt like a game of tug o' war.

I was a risk taker while Brad was cautious in certain matters (except for playing the stock market!). For instance, when I decided to quit my job to study full-time, Brad thought it was an unnecessary risk.

"Babes, how yuh going to manage without a steady income? Remember yuh have your expenses; plus, yuh still helping out yuh mother," he said.

And he was right; I may have moved out from Mom, but I had to help her maintain her household.

"I found a part-time data entry job at the Hilton. I'll work from 6pm to 11pm ... and they'll give me dinner."

Brad was not impressed when I told him how much I would make on the job.

"Remember I've also been saving to buy a car ... but

that can wait, so I'll use up some of that money too," I said.

I was convinced of the changes I had to make to further myself.

Brad thought it was just too risky. But, this decision left me free to pursue my course of choice, which the university only offered in the daytime. It was stressful, but it was worth all the effort.

I completed university less than two years after switching to full-time studies and graduated with honours. I was pleased that I had made some progress in my life. Brad stayed with me during this time, but there was no change in our relationship status. He continued setting his own unhurried pace to our lives. While studying, sometimes a week would pass before I saw him or heard from him. That did not bother me; I was busy.

Perhaps our relationship would move to the next level after I graduated.

Now a graduate of the University of the West Indies, with a major in International Relations (and a minor in Management Studies), I was even more attuned to the realities of political life in Jamaica. This continued to offer me some amount of distraction from my own 'soap opera' life.

It was a sad time in politics. Within a couple of years after reclaiming the political limelight and returning to the helm of power in 1989, Michael Manley fell ill. He had cancer. His image slowly changed from that of a fiery politician to one of an elder statesman. His illness forced him to pass the baton as party chief to his successor, Percival James (P.J.) Patterson and he demitted office before the end of his five-year term.

With this development, I reflected on Manley's political life and intentions. He had, in his own words, ". . . [challenged] the powers of Western economic structures". No one can dispute that he eradicated many backward colonial practices in Jamaica, which favoured the elite. He replaced them with policies that provided all Jamaicans with equal opportunities for self-improvement, such as greater access to education and housing.

I had learnt almost immediately on entering university in Introduction to Politics, that the hard times we experienced in the late 1970s were not entirely due to Manley's socialist policies, or even to alleged US/CIA interference. They were, instead, largely the result of external economic forces, primarily the 'oil shocks' directly linked to the rapid increases in oil prices on the world market during that period. The country was simply unable to keep up with the rising cost of purchasing oil and hence, could hardly manage its financial affairs as money was diverted from social programmes to buy fuel.

In 1992, Manley's early departure from office allowed P.J. Patterson, aka 'P.J.' or 'The Fresh Prince', to become Prime Minister. It was without much fanfare, perhaps because of the circumstances. Patterson was a lawyer by training and hailed from among the 95 percent of Jamaicans of African descent who populated our country, but that had very little to do with his rise to power. He was a senior PNP stalwart and cabinet member.

Patterson was a measured talker; not a charismatic orator like Michael Manley had been in his time. He had a quiet strength, a sharp intellect and was perceptive when it came to reading the mood of the country. He started out by working to disengage the country from what many scholars considered counterintuitive policies imposed on us by the IMF from the 1970s, again in the 1980s and through to the early 1990s.

Without the IMF hovering over him, Patterson decisively moved the Jamaican economy into its greatest period of liberalization since the 1960s. Patterson, though a socialist at heart, like the new Manley we had seen in the late 1980s, embraced the more liberal emerging political trends. Soon after he came to power, Jamaicans enjoyed the freedom of importing and buying anything from abroad that they pleased. The country was clearly on a different path than in the 1970s and early 1980s and perhaps, too, Patterson's easy-going nature made us feel unthreatened by ideology.

Indeed, while Patterson was in office, I observed first-hand, that he had his own allure. His strong presence bowled me over the first time I was in the same room with him.

I got the opportunity to attend two different types of events, with Brad, where 'P.J.' was host. The first of these random opportunities was at a political function in his constituency to celebrate the opening of a newly built road in Westmoreland, a parish at the western tip of Jamaica. He was jubilant and animated in delivering his address.

"Wesmoreland People, this is fi yuh time now! The new road pretty and it smooth," he jigged a bit as he said this, then gripped the improvised lectern with both hands, leaning forward on it to deliver his punchline.

"But the most important ting 'bout this new road is that it will allow yuh to travel in style and do yuh business and mek yuh money. Now yuh children can have a much better life."

Cheers went up for Patterson. The after-party consisted of upbeat *yaad* music and lots of curried goat and white rice. There was much jollification among the PNP comrades as they downed unlimited amounts of Wray & Nephew White Overproof Rum – neat, on the rocks or chased with whichever free beverages were available.

The second occasion I was near P.J. Patterson was at an informal private lyme at Laughing Waters – a government-owned villa, located on one of the most beautiful beachfront properties near Ocho Rios. He was there with some of his ministers, advisors and their project consultants (Brad being among the latter group). We seemed to have joined them after a meeting.

Prime Minister Patterson was wearing one of his dashiki

shirts, looking quite comfortable, as if guaranteed to come away with some inspiration for managing the country. Though he had his typical relaxed air about him, I sensed he was still talking about national matters. I felt privileged to have been so close to our prime minister – even though we had not exchanged a word except for cordial greetings, but I was impressed with his magnetism. He could easily have swayed me into joining his party. Such was his appeal; it left no doubt in one's mind that he was the leader of a cause.

By then, I had long decided against joining any political organization, given the constant news about the underbelly of Jamaican politics. I recognized that our politics was like two sides of a coin. One side was the glitz of good intentions while the other was divisiveness – *tribalism,* and that was disquieting to me. I would have to make my contribution to national development through other avenues. Early in his tenure, Prime Minister P.J. Patterson himself had set up the National Committee on Political Tribalism in 1996 to address the issues that were causing political tensions and violence. But it seemed entrenched.

As the economy morphed from influences of strict socialism to liberalism under Patterson's guidance, other unofficial changes in the political structure emerged. One such was the rise of the "don" in communities as *de facto* party representatives, via the growth of a system called patron-clientelism or clientelism.

I will not pretend to be an expert on this matter. We

discussed this situation one day in our tutorial for Caribbean Political Systems. Tutorials were teaching sessions, usually led by tutors (assistant lecturers) to provide deeper insight into topics introduced in the general lectures. They usually began with a student presenting what he or she had researched on a topic from the course. Today was my friend Richie Priestley's turn to present to the rest of us on 'The Impact of Community Dons'.

"Sir," he said to our tutor, who also happened to be the lecturer for the course, "I could hardly find any material on this topic. The late Professor Carl Stone seemed to have understood clientelism better than anyone else!"

"Ok. Carry on ... what's your source?"

Richie continued as instructed.

"I read Professor Stone's book, *Democracy and Clientelism in Jamaica* and I also skimmed a few newspaper articles on the subject, Sir." He continued,

"What I understand is that this is an informal arrangement that allows followers of the parties, especially the ruling party, to have more direct access to scarce national resources. This link is through certain political activists called dons, who have emerged as the go-between for the citizens and the state. The dons ensure the community members vote '*en bloc*' for the party they support."

"Why is this working?" the tutor asked Richie, who apparently thought he had finished his presentation and was moving to take his seat.

Richie stopped midway, looking puzzled as if, despite

his readings, he could not explain how this situation came to be.

"Alright, so though the voters do not officially elect the dons, they (the dons) derive their power from their connections with those in high public office. Some of them date back to the 1970s, when they were party activists defending the ideologies. Now, they are like brokers in the distribution of scarce benefits in Jamaica at the community level – like godfathers. Some say they are also involved in illicit activity, such as drug dealing and gun running. Some of them have more power and access to resources than politicians because of their association with the organized underworld."

"And this is exactly why the clientelism and don situation is becoming unmanageable in this country," the lecturer said,

"... It is a sinister side of our socio-political networking that has been operating as an institutionalized incentive scheme in our political system, its mantra being. 'if yuh vote fi mi, mi will fix yuh up'."

Just when I thought the tutor was getting carried away, Richie jumped in, trying to soften the point about the dons and their role in the society.

"Sir, some of them also try to do 'good works' by sharing the profits from their self-owned enterprises – whether legitimate or not – among the dispossessed in their communities. They are like safety nets for the garrisoned poor, doling out money to unemployed parents to assist them with taking care of their children . . ." It sounded as if he were reciting and the tutor looked less than impressed.

"So, . . . the point you want us to take away is that the people at the community level see the dons as do-gooders; not usurpers of the political system?"

Richie nodded, as if the point would have been lost if he spoke.

It was overwhelming for those not immediately exposed to this way of life.

And it was against this background, in the 1990s, that a third political party, the National Democratic Movement (NDM) was born. Its president Bruce Golding, former Chairman of the JLP. Bruce, son of Tacius Golding, a former Speaker of the House and himself a Parliamentarian for 25 years, was considered heir-apparent in the JLP. But, he was in no mood to wait indefinitely to succeed Edward Seaga as leader of the JLP. And Seaga was in no hurry to give up party leadership.

The NDM was Bruce's immediate opportunity to lead a political party.

It was now 1995. The original third party, the Marxist WPJ, had broken up soon after the beginning of the 1990s. The NDM exploded onto the political scene, buttressing the cries from civil society and human rights groups against corruption, crime and clientelism in Jamaica. Its stated intention should it get into office, would be to address these issues, mainly through amending the Jamaican Constitution, parts of which, the NDM said, had become irrelevant to addressing governance in a modern, independent Jamaica.

There were many radio interviews to publicize their vision and win public support. On one popular talk show, Mr Golding was asked some tough, direct questions about the value of the NDM to the Jamaican people.

"Mr Golding, what is the NDM offering to do for us?"

"Well . . . a lot," Golding said with certitude, "we have many reforms we want to undertake to make Jamaica a better democratic country. I'm going to list them out." He cleared his throat then began,

"We want to limit each elected prime minister to serving a maximum of two terms in office. And we want full disclosure of private contributions to political parties – to exclude corruption of this mechanism of party support."

"And," Bruce Golding continued with his list, "we also want to break ties with the UK Privy Council as the final court of appeal for Jamaicans."

"But why is that so important, Mr Golding?" the journalist asked. "Isn't it more important to focus on our economy rather than trying to fiddle with the constitution?"

There was a change to Golding's tone. Clearly this journalist did not see the link between the constitution and the people's welfare.

"You should not forget that we are an independent nation, therefore we must replace our archaic Westminster parliamentary system with a republican presidential model, like America's. That would be a more relevant democracy. Our model will give the people of Jamaica greater control over the political system."

With these grand declarations, the new party created only a minor stir. Most people seemed unconvinced that they could address the corruption and other matters they brought to the fore, but a few were hopeful. Maybe some people were still too sapped from the struggles of the late 1970s or too cynical after the unfulfilled expectations of the 1980s, and others too blinded by the *bling-bling* of the liberal 1990s to process the meaning of a 'new and different' kind of democracy.

Whatever the reason, not many saw the NDM as a viable alternative to the PNP or the JLP.

After all, Bruce had been second-in-command in the JLP.

People were asking,

"How 'new and different' could his politics possibly be from that of the old guard?"

Regardless, Golding zealously promised Jamaicans a recharged democracy if elected. He stoutly proclaimed that the NDM was the only solution for Jamaica. The PNP might have been the party for the poor and the JLP the party for the business class, but now the NDM was the party for all who truly wanted to advance Jamaica.

"Give us, Oh Lord, the sense to see
The path from which we ought to flee..." (NDM hymn)

~

While all these new political rearrangements were going on, the economy continued to open, as the state systematically reduced its role as the main player in the marketplace. By then, the policy of import substitution was largely forgotten as people no longer cared about "tunning our hands to mek fashion" as per Manley's doctrine. Rather, many Jamaicans were enjoying ready access to previously restricted imports of finished consumer items. There was more of everything, including bad debts. Though business people could freely borrow as much as they wanted to improve their businesses, expansion of industry and production remained low.

By 1997, the number of persons unemployed was at its highest ever in Jamaica. During this time, many unemployed persons set up informal businesses when they could not find jobs. They cited bureaucratic red tape as the reason for not registering their businesses; the process required too many steps and too much paperwork. These businesses were hidden; it was hard to say how much they were contributing to the economy, as they were not registered as formal businesses. It was hard to tax them. But it was equally hard to collect taxes from some of the more established, legitimate businesses. No one was helping the state to pay its bills.

Many ordinary Jamaicans were living extravagant lifestyles on whatever credit they could get. Eventually, the banks could not collect their outstanding debt. The economy was heading for a crash. It was an era of false prosperity.

The government moved to save the country by setting up the Financial Sector Adjustment Company (FINSAC), in 1997, to fix the woes of the financial sector – particularly the banks and insurance companies that had been operating without the benefit of a regulatory framework. A significant number of businesses went bankrupt when they could not repay the financial institutions, due to the high interest rate regime that had prevailed.

Cracks were now showing up in the theory that a free market economy would benefit the country and lead to the trickling down of wealth to the poor. This was not happening. There was an expectation that this economic model would create prosperity in the short-term, but too many people remained in the stranglehold of poverty. The free market approach had failed to smooth out our social inequalities.

It did not help that the crime levels had continued to rise during the time of financial crisis. We felt uneasy as it loomed over us and we were embarrassed because the lens of the global camera was zooming in and transmitting the tale worldwide.

Yet, we were a popular people – known for our warmth and friendliness to visitors and well recognized because of our enviable culture, world renowned for our reggae music and our cuisine. We could boast about our natural attractions such as our beaches and historic sites. The world joined us in singing praises to our superstars like Bob Marley, Jimmy Cliff, Merlene Ottey and others. So often, we were the toast of the world.

But our political culture was threatening to blot out our exclusive brand. It seemed that the Machiavellian philosophy, "Do good only as necessity requires", had replaced the ethos of uprightness expressed in our national anthem, "Justice, truth be ours forever..."

Living in Jamaica in the 1990s had its challenges, but was a good time for me. Indeed, I was fortunate to be among the educated and employed, despite the difficult economy.

I had recently started a new and exciting job as an airline sales executive with regional responsibilities for the Western Caribbean. Yes. I had returned to work in the industry I left to further my studies – but at a much higher level. I took advantage of the open economy and easy access to credit that was available just before the economy crashed, by getting myself a new car the very first day on the job. Even though I had been out of a job studying, I could afford to; not only because of my 'step-up in life' but also due to the easy access to credit.

Brad was very happy with my promotion. He became more attentive and more available – more like the old Brad I had first met.

On my birthday, Brad decided to take me out to celebrate in style. I was as curious as I was excited, as he was not often up for this sort of outing.

"Where we going?" I asked.

"Blue Mountain Inn," Brad responded. "My sister suggested it." He was all charm and smiles.

At that time, Blue Mountain Inn was among the few five-star restaurants in Jamaica. Situated in the Blue Mountain area, as the name suggests, its ambience surpassed superb.

I thought to myself,

"This must be the big night. Maybe he is going to propose."

Why else would Brad, who preferred casual attire outside of work, choose a formal restaurant that required that he wear a jacket, if it was not going to be *that* special night?

I dressed accordingly, wearing a flirty knee-length silk-blend red dress that I had bought overseas. Mom had long given up sewing, but she had adjusted the dress for me and now it was figure flattering. I completed the look with a swipe of red lip gloss, black strappy heels and a clutch purse.

The drive up to the restaurant was pleasant. On arrival, we were seated on the open terrace overlooking the city and offering a breathtaking view of the city lights.

We had a romantic dinner. I can still remember the taste of the buttery lobster melting on my tongue as I savoured the most delectable meal I had ever had, accompanied by the restaurant's best white wine. Brad enjoyed his meal of medium-rare steak and red wine, as much as I did mine. This could easily be one of the most romantic memories of my time spent with Brad – the elegant candlelight setting, and his display of charm, made me confident about his love for me.

Finally, it was the moment I had been waiting for all evening and for the last few years. I tried to conceal my excitement as Brad reached into his breast pocket and pulled out a compact jewellery box. As he opened the box, I caught a glimpse of something sparkly, but when I looked inside the box there was no engagement ring. It was a gold necklace.

I felt let down but still managed to smile.

"Thanks Brad ... I thought yuh were going to propose," I said hesitantly.

"Babes, yuh know how much yuh mean to me," Brad's voice petered out, leaving not too much that I did not already know, unsaid. He looked around and then looked at me as if he had given me all of Blue Mountain Inn and not just a night there. Why did I need a proposal?

With that, we wrapped up the night and left the restaurant.

I accepted that for now; this was all I would get from Brad – reassurance that he wanted to be with me, but not the ultimate commitment I craved.

I wanted family – one with mother, father and child.

After all these years, Brad still was not ready to settle down and have a family. Whenever the subject of marriage and family came up, he always indicated that he had something else to do before starting a family. He needed to build a house or buy a better piece of land, in a nicer location. I had waited patiently. But after so many years, was I hanging on to what was only a glorious promise of love?

A few months before my birthday the subject of marriage had come up.

"Brad," I had asked, "Are we ever going to get married?"

"Babes, why don't yuh just set the date," Brad had replied.

But his answer was not convincing enough for me to act on that cue. On Christmas Eve, we had gone browsing in a jewellery store and had stopped at the section with the engagement rings. I indicated the type of ring I liked. We left the store with a nice Fendi watch; I concluded that he would prefer to select the ring as a surprise.

The dream of walking down the aisle with Brad was rapidly fading and I laid the blame for his lack of desire to commit at my own feet. Self-doubt swirled in the mind. Maybe I had failed to demonstrate that I was the right woman for him – though I had tried hard each day to measure up to his expectations. He wanted me to be more down-to-earth, *rootsy*. Whatever Brad suggested I tried. But Brad's need to remodel me was just a delaying tactic; I would never be perfect. This had nothing to do with me. It was his own fear of surrendering to love.

After that near-heavenly night at Blue Mountain Inn, Brad and I continued with our very predictable relationship. I was not satisfied, but I was hesitant to step out and start a new relationship because I still loved him. Maybe I was being too impatient, but we had known each other for nearly 10 years. This was not what I had dreamt of at the beginning of our relationship. My life was spiralling without fulfilment. I needed to take control of its direction.

9

Reaching Deep Within

THE NEW YEAR STARTED WITH ME giving Brad an ultimatum. He had not been looking happy for the last few weeks anyway. He seemed very contemplative whenever we were together, and I was tired of being in limbo with him. He conceded that this was the right time for us to have a child. For me, this meant he was ready for us to become a real family and that he was ready to steer away from any flirtatious indulgence and commit to me fully.

Within a couple of months after my talk with Brad about our future, I was pregnant. My patience with this relationship was about to bear fruit! It was as if Brad and I had spoken this baby into being by letting the Universe know that we both wanted the same thing at the same time! It was a miracle.

I went to the doctor and he confirmed the miracle. That evening, I could not wait to show Brad the positive (+) result from the pregnancy test taken at the doctor's office. When he arrived at my apartment, he let himself in. He eased his work boots off at the bedroom door as I bounced towards him, test results in hand, awaiting his reaction. Brad stared for a long time at the proof of pregnancy I presented to him. I sat on the edge of the bed, waiting for perhaps a hug and him doing something akin to the *Bossa Nova* dance. Then he said, in a very matter-of-fact tone,

"Babes I'm still not ready for this; I need to straighten out my life. But I hope it's a boy."

What?! The baby's sex was the last thing on my mind!

"Is this all yuh can come up with Brad? Yuh hope it's a boy?"

Well yuh know what, … since yuh not ready for this, just leave!"

"Babes …," he was reaching for an explanation, but I did not give him a chance to finish.

"Just go! Go!" I screamed, louder than I had ever done in his presence.

Brad tried to grab my arms to pacify me. "Go-o-o …"

my voice crackled, "Just go!"

Brad slipped his shoes back on and started toward the front door.

I ran ahead of him to open it and he hastened out – not a word said, as if he were afraid to tarry, lest I attack him. He had never seen me so irate.

I slammed the door behind him, seething.

This was not the time for tears.

I would do this on my own.

The first few months of my pregnancy were difficult in

many ways. After my meltdown with Brad, communication between us changed; he barely spoke when he came by my apartment to check how I was doing. I was also very ill – my morning sickness lasting the entire day.

I decided to wait before telling my family members and friends the good news.

Apart from Brad, only two other persons knew what was happening in my first trimester. The first was Naomi, who had made the doctor's appointment for me and accompanied me on my visit to confirm the pregnancy. The second was Mom, who I told the good news only after it was confirmed. It was a Saturday afternoon and we were sitting at the breakfast table in her kitchen having some chicken foot soup. I could hardly keep it down because I was so queasy.

"Mother," I said, after my first few spoons of soup, "I have a surprise for yuh."

"Surprise?" Mom said, perhaps thinking it was some sort of gift.

"Yes," I said. "It's a little surprise – one that will cry and laugh and play and grow."

"What! What yuh saying to me Sanaa? Yuh mean you're expecting?"

Mom jumped up, her spoon clattering on the soup bowl as she pushed back her chair to come and hug me.

She knew how much I wanted a child.

"Brad must be very happy! I guess yuh getting married soon?"

"No; no that's not going to happen. The only thing he

cares about right now is that the baby will be a boy."

Mom, though looking a little peeved at my revelation, assured me that Brad would come around.

"Just give him a little time. Both of yuh have been together for so long. Why shouldn't he be ready to settle down now?"

That, I could not answer. But he had tried since the last blow up at my apartment to apologize for his "state of mind".

We soon forgot about Brad and his nonchalance. Mom dived into tips about what to expect during the pregnancy and how to eat to get the right nourishment.

At the end of my first trimester, it was time for me to share the good news about my pregnancy to all. Karen figured out what was happening with me, when I bumped into her one evening at Naomi's house. After living f or many years in Kingston, she had moved back to St Elizabeth with her family just before I became pregnant. She had come into town to attend to some business and here I was, a little plumper now than when she had last seen me.

"Sanaa, don't tell me you're. . .?"

Smiling, she gushed on, looking very pleased.

"Good. It's about time!"

Naturally, she was happy for me, knowing that all I ever wanted was a family. We were like schoolgirls catching up on the most recent round of gossip, but our chatter was mostly about my pregnancy. It felt good seeing Karen, and since she was returning to the country the next day, we made a date for the next time she came to Kingston.

Karen and I managed to see each other a couple of times during my pregnancy and, after I gave birth, we made plans for her to spend a Saturday with us when she came to Kingston.

During my pregnancy, Brad took care of me in his own way, though he kept any excitement he may have been feeling in check. His support entailed going grocery shopping for me. I would get extremely nauseous at the smell of detergent from as far as the supermarket parking lot. He would also drive me out of town for work and do other little errands with me as he saw fit – but all in silence, as if he had joined a cult that required this type of vow.

Gwen Stefani's hit song, "Don't Speak" from a couple years before, constantly played in my head – as if just released.

I did not ask Brad for the reason behind his non-communicativeness. Instead, I focused on my pregnancy. It was difficult, but I pushed myself and continued travelling across the country and internationally, as required.

At the end of my second trimester, I took a personal weekend trip to Miami to shop for the baby. I stayed with Brad's eldest sister and both she and her daughter took me shopping. The baby's sex had remained unrevealed, even after two ultrasounds; so, everything was going to be in either yellow or green, until after the delivery.

I returned the Sunday evening feeling tired and retired to bed early. I woke up in the middle of the night to get some milk and noticed that the usual gymnastics in my stomach were absent.

"Little darling, are you Ok?" I asked, rubbing my stomach.

There was no movement. I stood in front of the open refrigerator, gulping my milk, waiting for a kick. Nothing happened.

I returned to bed and tried to go back to sleep, but sleep would not come. I was too worried to fall asleep, as the baby was always very active – especially after I ate.

Next morning, I got up early. There was still no movement from the baby. Alarmed, I called Brad.

"Brad, the baby not moving!"

There was a short pause. Brad was often calmer than me.

"How long since he hasn't moved?" Brad asked, concerned.

"Since last night," I responded. "I'm going to call the doctor now."

"Ok," Brad said. "Let me know what he says."

I hung up and called the doctor instantly. He was happy that I had called – he had tried to reach me on the weekend when I was away – the results from my last blood test had come back, indicating that I had high amounts of sugar in my blood. I had gestational diabetes. He was out of office now but Dr Samuels, his partner, would see me on his behalf. I went in to see her immediately.

I had barely eaten for the first four months of pregnancy because of prolonged morning sickness. As soon as I could digest food, Mom would prepare lunch for me – usually something with fish, but sometimes I got my request for meat, as I was experiencing a craving for beef and pork.

"Dr Samuels, please explain to me what caused me to develop this illness," I demanded, when she advised me I had to be admitted to the hospital for a few days.

"Miss Wallenston," she explained patiently, "these are just typical diseases associated with pregnancy for women who are 30 and over. It doesn't matter what you eat; however, if you have a family history of diabetes, you are more susceptible to this illness."

I checked both boxes. No use arguing with the doctor. I had to go into the hospital. The baby was at risk.

I left the doctor's office in a daze from this news. I passed by my office to notify them that I had to go to the hospital, but I needed to pause to process my diagnosis. The remedy was heavy doses of insulin and a restricted diet – basically void of sugary foods.

After leaving my office, I went home and hurriedly packed my bag. Brad met me at home and drove me to the hospital, the situation breaking his silent treatment. With his baby at risk, Brad's memory seemed to have tripped back.

"Sanaa," Brad said, holding my hand in his. "I don't think yuh need to worry. I'm sure you're just going in for observation and to stabilize yuh blood sugar."

I sighed and nodded in agreement.

We went straight to Nutthall Memorial Hospital, an old private hospital built in the 20th century by the British. It was situated in what was, in those times, the urban centre of the city, called Cross Roads. It was very peaceful at Nutthall, contradicting the chaos of whatever was going on inside my body. My regular doctor was waiting, ready to check me in and, immediately, I got my first dose of insulin.

Later in the evening, Brad brought me a TV and some magazines, so I could be comfortable during my hospital stay. Over the next two days, my doctor ordered increasingly higher dosages of insulin for me, but the sugar levels in my blood remained unresponsive to the treatment. He was concerned; there was only faint movement in my womb. If this continued, he would have to take the baby as early as 28 weeks into gestation. The baby would have to stay in the hospital for close observation.

"No way," I said.

How could I possibly leave my baby in a hospital all by him or herself in his or her first weeks of life?

At the end of the week, stronger poking in my stomach was testament that my blood sugar level had improved. The blood tests, however, indicated it was not back to normal, but my doctor allowed me to check out of the hospital. I would need to self administer the insulin three times daily by inserting a needle into my thigh, carefully aiming the medicine under the skin. I also had to visit the doctor weekly until he delivered the baby, by Caesarean section.

Brad decided to be fully present for me during the last trimester.

He met me at the doctor's office each Thursday afternoon at 2pm. There, he would give the doctor an account of everything that I was eating, while they discussed between themselves the pros and cons of me consuming each food item, as if I was not in the room. This went on for two months and then, at week 37 into my pregnancy, it was time for us to meet our baby.

Brad took me to the hospital on the Thursday evening before my scheduled delivery. Next Friday morning he came back early, though in his words, he was not "brave enough" to be with me in the operating theatre.

"I can't deal with the sight of the blood," he said.

After the nurses prepared me for surgery and took me to the operating theatre, the last thing I remembered was the doctor telling me to count backwards from 10 to one; I got to about eight as the anaesthesia took over.

When I awakened, Brad was still at the hospital. I had never seen him so happy or so proud as that moment when he announced that we had a baby boy. We were both happy the baby had arrived safely, considering what I had gone through leading up to delivery.

Shortly after I woke up, a nurse brought my baby to me bundled up, his little eyes squeezed tightly closed. I was relieved to have him out of my belly and into my arms. I tried to breastfeed him but did not have much luck. My milk was not flowing; it required time and some practice.

We needed to name our son. We had a short list of both boy and girl names picked out as we still had no idea what we were having up to delivery time. We had decided to wait to see the baby to determine which name fit best.

We knew instantly that we would call him Kai.

He was just a miniature life form – completely dependent on us, yet already bringing so much joy to our lives.

I said, "Hello Kai," and his eyes opened instantaneously, as if he recognized my voice and his name. Wow! That was amazing. It was as if he knew he was finally in his mommy's arms.

Kai and I remained in the hospital for four days post-delivery so that they could supervise his progress. They confined him to an incubator, except for breastfeeding. They also wanted to ensure my blood sugar was returning to normal levels.

Throughout our stay, our hospital room was constantly a-buzz with visitors bringing gifts and flowers. Amidst all the "oohs", "aahs", and congratulations from family members, friends and associates, I was exhausted – worn out from the ravages of anaemia and gestational diabetes. The fatigue threatened to rob me of my maternal bliss, but I was determined to welcome my guests on their arrival and to nurse Kai as best as I could.

When I was discharged from the hospital four days after giving birth, Brad had a surprise for me.

"Sanaa, I'm coming to stay with yuh and the baby at

the apartment," he announced. He had found us a more spacious apartment just before the baby was born.

"Oh . . . really?" I said flatly.

"I'll just be there for a while," he continued.

He wanted to be near his newborn so that he could get a chance to bond with him. He would help me manage the baby while I was recovering from the surgery. And, he said,

"Maybe there will be another chance for us."

I had no answer to his last bit of reasoning for moving in with us.

By that time, I had weaned myself off Brad.

"No *freakin'* way," I told myself, would he have another chance of disappointing me.

I was happy that Brad was happy with the birth of his brand new, shiny baby boy. After all the time we had spent together, he was still clueless about what I had really wanted. I would be a fool to get my hopes up for having a family life with Brad. I was tired and wary of his seesaw approach to love.

My new attitude was not lost on Brad when he moved in. We had never discussed the reason for his emotional disengagement from me when I was pregnant; it remained like a wedge between us, blocking any possibility of closeness. We compensated by being over-attentive to Kai, but otherwise, we were just striving for harmony as new parents with our child's best interest in mind.

This lasted only for a short while. After an argument one Saturday afternoon, based purely on semantics, Brad took most of his clothes and the hangers he had brought them on and moved out. He would collect the other pieces later. The argument came dangerously close to the point about why he had clammed up leading to Kai's arrival. Brad was not ready to discuss the matter, so he left. Emotionally I had moved on anyway, so I was unaffected by his departure.

There was some uncertainty about the way forward for me. For a long time, he had been a constant feature of my life. I had moved from experiencing electrifying and then agonizing love for Brad to accepting that there would be no 'happily ever after' for us. What was left of the once overflowing love I had for him had drained from my battered heart.

But not having to figure out how Brad really felt about us, or who he may be with, left me free to do more thinking about my own life and to reflect on the years that had elapsed since Jay's passing.

In his last letter to me, Jay's final advice was,

"Sanaa, in everything you do, let God direct your path."

I had not listened to that inner voice that kept telling me that I was forcing myself into a structure that was not going to work for me. Chasing after Brad's acceptance and approval had left me crumpled and worn.

Only my faith in God could restore me.

Though I was no longer involved in church the way I used to be as a young adult, I still felt that there was a higher power available to me whenever my human strength felt depleted. I reached out to the Divine Power through prayer and He stepped in to help me. He rejuvenated me when I felt too exhausted to keep up with the physical demands of being a new mother, and He made sure that I got all the support I needed from family and friends in this new and challenging period of my life.

Thankfully, Tony, who had been living in Montego Bay with his wife, had moved back to Kingston just before Kai's birth. We had always remained close and he was as much a friend as a brother to me during this period. He had no children; so, he was happy to have his new nephew.

And, as usual, Mom was there more than ever to give me her undiluted love, which was exactly what I needed.

In December 1997, six weeks after Kai was born, P.J. Patterson was re-elected, with a large margin of victory at the polls. It was his second election victory, with the previous being in 1993.

Sadly, Manley had died in the spring of 1997. He was not around to witness his party's consecutive victory at the polls.

I wondered how the PNP would keep the party's core socialist philosophy alive while acquainting themselves with modern liberal politics. Only time would reveal this. Patterson's win sent a message to the JLP (and the NDM) that the people were comfortable with his mode of politics.

It was a significant time for Jamaica's electoral process – touted as the most peaceful since 1980 and reflecting the level of global peace and cooperation seen only since the ushering in of the New World Order, in a post-Cold War era.

Though I did not pay much attention to the happenings at the time because of my maternal preoccupation, I was aware that there were little or no shenanigans from the parties during their campaigns leading to the election. There was even less trickery from desperate party supporters to influence the outcome of the elections, through the 'selling and buying' of votes and stuffing of ballot boxes with bogus votes.

Even more significant was the fact that there were very few politically motivated murders reported during the campaign period, compared with previous elections, especially that of 1980. It was a sign of maturity among the electorate in Jamaica that was long overdue. We were finally rejecting political violence, the 'win-at-any-cost' approach to politics.

I settled into my new life – a proud mother. My relationship with Brad was finally over – moribund as far as I was concerned. He came by my home only to enjoy his son. It was amazing to see Kai developing so rapidly. He had started walking before he was eight months old and was quite alert and intelligent beyond his age. He was a very healthy baby. So far, he had had a runny nose only once, which had lasted a few days.

The weekend before his first birthday was different. When I got home that Friday evening, he did not run to greet me at the door as he always did. He had a low-grade temperature and his nanny said he had been droopy after his afternoon nap. I gave him some fever reducer and tried to make him comfortable for the night. By next morning, the fever got worse and Brad took the baby to see his sister-in-law, who was a paediatrician. Kai was apparently having a mild case of tonsillitis; this was a first for him.

On the Sunday, I was due to leave for a business trip to New York for two days. I delayed my departure by a day, although I knew that he would be safe with his father, who always took care of him when I travelled. Kai's nanny would care for him in the day until Brad took over after 5pm. Even so, I wanted to be sure that Kai was feeling better before I left. While away, I checked up on him several times a day. The doctor had given him antibiotics, so I expected the fever to subside. But it did not. I was quite alarmed when on returning, Tony, who came to pick me up at the airport, only responded with a deep sigh when I asked about Kai's progress.

"Bwoy, Sanaa," Tony said, after a few moments of anxious silence between us,

"I don't know how to tell yuh this, but yuh baby really very sick; the fever not going down."

"What yuh mean?" I demanded. "I don't understand. I thought he was getting better; up to last night he was getting better."

I burst out crying. I felt like I was in a pressure cooker. The car felt heavily compressed by the weight of my exasperation with this persistent fever.

Tony did not know what to say to console me but tried.

"We didn't want yuh to worry, but Brad just took him back to the doctor."

"Let's go," I squealed. "Let's go!"

Tony was already driving in the direction of the Kids Klinic but sped up to get us there in next to no time from the airport. He had barely parked before I rushed out of the car and into the doctor's office, taking the steps to the first floor of the building two at a time, but Kai was gone when I got there – his father was already at the Bustamante Children's Hospital with him.

Without any hesitation, Tony and I sped from Kids Klinic and headed for the hospital, disregarding the blaring car horns protesting our reckless speeding.

We got to the admissions section of the hospital in record time. When I found Kai, he was in the head nurse's arms. He looked shockingly thin. What was happening to my baby?

Kai had lost quite a bit of what his Uncle Theo referred to as his Sumo wrestler weight in the two-and-a-half days I had been away. He was wearing only his Huggies diaper as they had removed his clothes to help keep his little body cool. He looked so tiny as he reached for me – offering a weak smile and hanging on to me – desperate for relief from his discomfort. Kai nestled into my chest, searching for the familiar thumping of my heart, as I took a seat beside Brad on a bench inside the admission area. I kissed and cuddled my baby and tried to soothe him, feeling guilty that I had left him when he was so ill.

Then as we waited, we overheard the doctors discussing his ailment. Someone said "kawa-something".

"What is that, Doctor?" I asked, frantically jumping to my feet, still holding Kai. "What did you just say is wrong with him?"

They train medics to remain calm, but I cannot say I appreciated that right then. I could sense that they were sympathetic, but still not divulging anything they did not have to disclose before they were sure. After much discussion amongst themselves, they addressed us.

"We'll have to do a lumbar puncture," one of the doctors said. "We're checking for meningitis, you know … to rule that out if possible."

There was a lump in my throat, blocking my attempted response. Brad stood beside me, agitatedly seeking clarification from the doctors about the test. The nurse who was holding Kai when I got to the hospital took him from my tight clutch and headed for the treatment room. I tried to follow but they stopped me. A heavy grey door leading to the sterile-looking room closed behind the nurse holding Kai – shutting me off from comforting my son.

It was horrible hearing Kai screaming as they stuck the needle in his back to extract the fluid to do their test. He must have wondered how his parents had allowed a bunch of people he did not even know, to carry out such an intrusive procedure on him without any protest. Kai was helpless, and it must have seemed to him that we were too.

The wait for the diagnosis was long and extremely nerve-wracking. For his first night in the hospital, we had to bathe Kai repeatedly in icy water, to break the fever. He was strung up with a feeding tube and given strong antibiotics through an IV. No one would tell us what was happening to our son, after confirming that it was not meningitis.

Nearly a week after his hospitalization, the diagnosis came: Kai had contracted a rare and potentially life-threatening illness; a relatively unknown disease this side of the world, called Kawasaki Syndrome. No one knew exactly how he got it. Worse, was the fact that treatment was not available in Jamaica and too many days had passed before they had made the diagnosis for the very expensive single-dose medicine, immunoglobin, administered intravenously, to be effective.

The disease would have to run its course.

Kai spent his first birthday in the hospital – not a happy time for any of us. Who would have known that a mere sore throat and fever would have landed him in the hospital, fighting for his little life? I wanted to take his place, to spare him the agony he was experiencing. I wondered if an unknown force was orchestrating some special punishment for me. Where was the God I knew? When would He come to our rescue?

Even if I had sinned unforgivably, Kai was innocent.

Kai was in the hospital for over a week. Brad was with him each day, each night. I was in and out of the hospital day and night, but still going to work even though my company had given me compassionate leave. Tony sat in for me a couple of nights, insisting that I get proper rest. However, I did not sleep. I only cried and prayed. None of that seemed to work and we felt crushed when, after the doctors discharged Kai from the hospital, they had to readmit him within two days; he had regressed.

I waited for what seemed like an eternity for Kai to show some definitive sign that he was overcoming this terrible illness. During the wait, my conversations with God seemed one-sided. I wondered if He had heard my tears and prayers at all. He had. And when our son started pulling through, I thanked God for His mercy.

We knew Kai was back with us when he ate his first meal after three weeks – corned beef and cabbage. We had tried feeding him every day with different dishes after the nurses removed his feeding tube, but to no avail. That day, when the older kids were being fed and he pointed at them, we realized he was ready to eat. When he took a spoonful, we knew that he had crossed over to us safely from the brink of wherever it was that he had dangerously teetered for weeks.

Finally, I could take my baby home.

After Kai's recovery, I realized that his illness had taken a physical, emotional and spiritual toll on me. I decided to slow down and devote all my available non-working time to him. We might have missed celebrating his birthday in the traditional style, but I would celebrate his life.

I had begun postgraduate studies just a couple of months before Kai became ill and it felt like I had been running in a steeplechase all that time – having a travelling job, trying to keep up with a fast-paced degree programme, and attending to the demands of a young baby, almost single-handedly.

I would have to give up something and, naturally, the studies had to give way. In fact, they had already given way, so I took a leave of absence from school. During this hiatus, I reflected on how blessed I was to have such a marvellous child bestowed on me and for him to be spared long-term brain damage and coronary artery disease associated with this illness, especially without the benefit of the recommended drugs. His follow-up treatment required a daily dose of aspirin for six months to fix his dilated arteries.

After the six-month period, an echocardiograph revealed that Kai's arteries had returned to their normal size; he had fully recuperated. That was all that mattered after his illness. It was even more wonderful now to wake up to him, come home to him and just spend quality time with him. Kai would fall asleep in my arms almost every night when he was a toddler. Each night I would read him a story and then sing him one of the funny songs I had made up just for him, while watching him slowly drift off to sleep.

These snapshots remain hallowed in my mind.

The deepest and most fulfilling love is, without a doubt, the love of a mother for her child and I thank God that my experience with this profound love was not short-lived.

I looked forward to the task of raising a healthy and happy child in the coming years.

My life appeared to be returning to some level of normality, but not for long.

It was the week leading up to my birthday in March 1999, when I got a call from Naomi. She had gone to work at a hotel in Negril and I had not seen her for a few months. I was excited to hear from my friend, thinking it was an early birthday call.

Naomi spoke in a frayed voice.

"San, it's Karen …"

It was not going to be good news – I could tell as her voice broke.

"What happened?" I interjected, bracing myself. I had not seen Karen for almost a year.

"San … she died this morning."

Had I heard her correctly?

"What? Oh God … No … !" I let out a piercing wail, which forced one of my colleagues from an adjoining office to come running over to see what was wrong.

"How did this happen?" I managed to croak upon finding my voice.

She had been complaining of a headache for a couple of days and that morning it became excruciating, just as she was about to take her children to school. Her family rushed her to the hospital, but the doctors were unable to save her. Karen had had a brain aneurysm. It had erupted.

The news hit like a tsunami – unexpected, inexplicable and devastating. It was not easy to process. I did not want to believe it . . . Karen was too young, too vibrant and had too much to offer the world to go so soon.

I still miss Karen – her fresh perspective on love and her positive outlook on life. I often dream of her when things are topsy-turvy in my life. There, she remains youthful and vibrant, and she never fails to cheer me up. I will always thank God for loaning me such a gentle friend, full of light.

In my brief lifetime, I had weathered more than my fair share of losing loved ones. I felt enormously blessed that my son's life had been spared. God knows I would not have survived such a loss.

The recent scare of almost losing Kai did not bring Brad and me any closer. We continued with our separate lives, with Kai as our only connection. Often, Brad would spend time with Kai at my place but, on a few occasions, Kai would go and stay with him on the weekend. During the times that Brad came by to visit Kai, I remained convinced that there was something major in his life that he was keeping from me because he was always so cagey.

It took almost three years for me to get confirmation that my intuition was on target. Brad's admission to what he was hiding from me was, as usual, not voluntary. I had to put bits and pieces of information from various sources together for the hidden pieces of his life to fall into place. And what a bombshell it was when it all came together!

Brad had fathered another child, a daughter, just before we had Kai.

And there was more.

Kai and his sister Hannah-Jade were already close – they had been meeting for play dates, unknown to me, when he spent weekends with his father.

Now I knew what I needed to know, but why the secrecy on Brad's part?

"Brad, yuh have a daughter," it was more a statement from me than a question, one evening when he came by to visit Kai.

He looked cornered.

"Yes or no", I said, when he just looked back at me.

"Yuh didn't expect me to find out?"

"I didn't know how to tell yuh Sanaa. I know yuh would be mad."

"But I should have known yuh would deal with her proper," Brad continued. "I see how yuh are with children."

His confession was powerful enough to temporarily reopen the wound he had so deftly carved into my heart before Kai was born. I had to pray to God to make me resolute in my decision to keep rancour away and just to be thankful for the positives in my life. After all, we were over.

I met Kai's sister within two weeks of Brad's admission. I'm not going to pretend that it was easy, but that adorable little girl came into my house and hugged me as if it were the most natural thing to do. How could I not embrace her? No way could I hold this child against Brad.

Just months after Brad's secret was out, he would have the chance to demonstrate that he felt freed by his confession. By then, Kai was finishing preschool and heading for kindergarten and a lot had changed in my life. Most significantly, I had become a statistic of downsizing, due to restructuring of the airline for which I had been working. I was jobless.

When I told Brad, he had a solution.

"Sanaa, yuh and Kai should move in with me," he suggested.

I thought through his suggestion. He had remained a devout bachelor and there was more than enough space in his home for both of us.

"But I have enough money to take me through for a while," I replied.

"Yuh don't have to worry. Yuh'll have your own bedroom." And he added, "I'll manage all the expenses related to running the house and providing for Kai until yuh find a job."

That was a magnanimous gesture on Brad's part. Having come clean about his life, Brad now felt emboldened – reaching out to make up for his dodginess. He was grateful that I did not rehash how much he had hurt me.

"Bwoy Brad, thanks, but I have to think about this."

I had misgivings about the wisdom of the living arrangement Brad had suggested, but after another couple of months without a job, I took up his offer. Kai and I moved into Brad's house to *kotch* with him.

I had made an application to buy a house in a new housing development called Long Mountain, more than a year before the job issue arose.

When I finally got the invitation to make the deposit to secure my house, it came nearly two months after I was out of work. Poof! Nothing can explain how my blighted anticipation of home ownership felt. It was a major disappointment. I had plans to expand the house when I took possession so that my mom could join me there. But what lending institution would have granted me a mortgage without a steady income?

I moved out of my apartment reluctantly and into Brad's house over the long Easter weekend, telling myself not to get too comfortable there.

After Kai and I settled in, Brad started showering me with overtures of love. It was unexpected.

"Brad, thanks again for letting us move here, I'm really grateful that I don't have to worry about rent until I find a job."

"Don't worry about it, babes, I'm just happy to have my family together."

I smiled sweetly at him as I did a mental eye-roll. I was happy he was happy. But my heart, now hermetically sealed, remained untouched by these words. I would wait to see how long his 'love' would last this time. Brad was doing his best to act like a family man and I played along. We started doing things like a family.

I picked up Kai from school in the afternoons and had dinner ready when Brad got home in the evenings, so we all ate together. On weekends, we took Kai to swimming and karate classes, shopped together and visited family members with our son in tow. Hannah-Jade spent some weekends and holidays with us and she and Kai had fun times together. Kai was happy, but I was itching to get back to work; to be independent.

I wanted to have income and not be completely dependent on Brad.

"Brad, what yuh think of me doing a little 'buying and selling'?"

Brad was working at his computer and paused to look at me with knitted brows, as if he found my suggestion preposterous.

"What yuh have in mind?"

"Oh . . . I could go to Panama where clothes are comparatively cheap and I would make a profit, easily." I said.

I had previously visited Panama with my friend Corine, who worked with another airline. I saw that there were many deals in Panama. Many Jamaican vendors were doing business there.

"Corine is going to get me a discounted pass for travel too."

"Whatever yuh feel will work is worth a try." Brad replied.

He seemed a little more convinced when I mentioned the discounted fare. He also offered to give me an advance to help with the purchases. I did not have to use up all my savings.

I went off to Panama to start my retail business. The trip was like a working vacation, as I needed a breather after my life changes. I came back with a suitcase full of women's workwear and sleepwear. I also bought some cute play clothes for Kai. The clothes sold quickly, as I kept the prices at introductory rates. However, after I paid back the advance and did the math, I barely broke even.

"Babes, why yuh don't just go back to the airlines or try another type of company," Brad said. "And at least, if yuh working with the airlines, it will help with the cost of travel if yuh still want to do the business."

He was right. But I did not see myself doing this buying and selling for the long term – the market was saturated with persons selling the very same products.

I needed a new experience in the corporate world. I decided to resume my studies to make myself more competitive in my job search. This would also assist me in extending my career options, after being in the airline industry for nearly 13 years. The decision required me to invest a substantial amount of my savings into this venture and, when I told Brad of my intentions, he flatly disagreed with my decision to resume my studies at that time. It was the evening after Kai's fourth birthday party. We had gone upstairs to retire for the night. I decided this was a good time to talk in detail about the course I had actually started at the university and that it would last a year, full-time.

"Sanaa, why yuh need to go back to school when yuh already have a degree and good management experience?" He asked. "Tell me," he insisted, "Why yuh going to spend money on another degree when there is a greater need for bringing in income?"

"Yuh don't understand," I said. "Higher qualifications will give me an edge in the business world! Nowadays everyone in the types of jobs I would want have a master's degree." I went on, "I just want to finish what I started three years ago." My voice trailed off.

But Brad's position was final. His jaws clenched tightly before he erupted,

"*Raas,* Sanaa!" "Yuh just not thinking. There is no need for all this studying and spending in lean times!"

Then he grabbed his already packed out-of-town bag, ran down the stairs, marched out of the house, jumped into his car and sped away.

Brad did not return until the next day after work.

That heated discussion was all I needed to realize that Brad had not changed. He only saw things his way and would not entertain any compromise. Neither had I changed. And I was bent on completing my studies this time around.

This ended our truce. From there on, Brad and I fought over most things, and agreed on nothing. This was *déjà vu.*

While studying, I managed to pick up a part-time teaching job in an associate degree programme at a new university in Kingston. I still could not afford to go out on my own because it did not pay me enough to cover my living expenses. Kai was also enjoying the two-parent lifestyle – so I kept up the façade despite Brad and I being at odds.

To those looking on who did not know the inside story, Brad and I may have looked like the perfect loving couple. I admitted to myself, however, that there was no use keeping up the pretense just for Kai's sake. This was not the truth about who we were and it was no way to live. It was as if I had suffered a relapse into a senseless addiction.

If I were to be a good mother and an effective professional, I would need to confront my weaknesses within. Perhaps what I was enduring was all a necessary lesson for getting me to a higher level of understanding about the way the Universe works. The Universe gives us whatever we are willing to passively accept – whatever we are willing to condone in our lives.

I needed to start over.

I read Iyanla Vanzant's *The Value in the Valley*, and I sought professional help from a life coach to prepare myself for a new career and life.

After my first coaching session I went home, I looked in the mirror and I said sternly to myself,

"Sanaa, yuh only going to get through this difficult time by reaching deep within to find the courage that lies dormant inside. Yuh've done this before."

I continued staring into my own eyes, saying,

"Yuh can do it again."

But what did that mean? It meant not swimming against the tide of my own life. It meant finding a way out of my labyrinth of co-dependency and courageously stepping out onto the new path that lay before me – one filled with the dignity of independence even in the face of financial struggles. And it would mean letting go of Brad as my crutch, without being afraid of falling, even if I needed to hobble forward on my own.

I was grateful to Brad for the lodging he was offering me; but I did not have to accept his dogma.

With this new mindset, I plotted my next move. I would search ardently for a nine-to-five in any arbitrary field then take the first job offer. I needed to build up my emergency savings and move out from Brad's place, even if I had not finished my studies. Going back to my mother's house was never an option. There was already enough going on there with her helping Gary raise his kids. I was more than welcome to stay with Tony if I needed to, but I did not want to be dragging Kai from place to place every few months. I would just have to bide my time before making a clean break from my phony existence.

In the broader scheme of things, I was not the only one who was doing some introspection.

The JLP had also lost yet another election and I surmised Edward Seaga must have been going through a similar self-examination as I, as he was blamed for the loss.

The election came near the end of 2002. Still leader of the JLP, Seaga had again gone up against P.J. Patterson, the PNP's leader. Eddie's campaign premise during the election was that under Patterson's leadership, government scandals (questionable use of state funds) were mounting.

"Under the PNP, corruption taking over the society.

"And yuh don't have to look hard to see that it is the very same PNP Government that leading the corruption." Seaga continued his point, "They not fighting it …they prefer go 'round the very system that set up to help us fight corruption …"

He was referring to the anti-corruption commission he had established back in 1986. It was an attempt to ensure transparency and fairness when issuing permits, licenses and government contracts to the private sector.

"So is time for Eddie to turn things around again …"

The JLP bells rang out with supporters shouting, "… shower, shower, shower!!!", endorsing his bid.

However, the electorate saw no need for a change in government, for choosing the JLP, irrespective of the check-list of PNP scandals that Seaga had compiled and presented to them, or even after the rapturous return of their political prodigal, Bruce Golding, to boost up his former party.

Losing this election – his fourth loss in a row – must have been a hard pill for Seaga to swallow. Accepting defeat is never easy in any sphere of life.

Anecdotal postmortems on Seaga's political life concluded that he was unable to win elections after the 1980s, because there was no longer any fear of communism in Jamaica. Some had posited that Seaga's authoritarian style had cost him his political power. Jamaicans supposedly prefer a charismatic leader – one they could 'connect with' and one who made them feel good.

Charismatic or not, perhaps Patterson's style was more favourable to the majority at that time because the PNP were now standing closer to the middle-ground in their political ideology. Conversely, Seaga's zealous style would have been viewed as over-the-top by the year 2002.

As we entered the 21st century, the debate between Seaga and Patterson, about who could best manage the country, raged on. From all indicators, after nearly two decades of dismal performance, the economy had started showing signs of growth. There were positive social indicators, including a reduction in the number of people living below the poverty line.

The PNP had also implemented what they referred to as "solid achievements", such as the new, efficient, state-of-the-art highway linking the city of Kingston to the island's south coast. There were also significant advances in our technology infrastructure, which far surpassed that of other islands in the hemisphere and facilitated the development of the ICT industry in Jamaica. Also coming up was the privatization of the Sangster International Airport in Montego Bay, our Tourism Mecca, for renovation to world-class standards. Some would say these were good enough reasons to keep a party in power. Why switch allegiance when things were improving?

Well, whether the PNP's achievements were the reason for not choosing Seaga as leader after the 1980s, the people he had delivered 20 years earlier had moved on into the new millennium without him. He had made his own mark on the nation in various ways, including the establishment of key institutions and organizations, like the National Training Agency and Jamaica Promotions Corporation. But he had to let go of the dream to lead the nation one last time. In the 1970s, Seaga had stood up for those who feared democratic socialism and communism.

But these were different times.

10

The Final Curtain Call

IT WAS RIGHT AFTER THESE PONDERINGS about the developments in my country, after I finally came to grips with some underlying truths about my own choices, that I decided to take the necessary step to move out of Brad's house, and on with my life.

A few days into January 2003, weeks away from me moving, I was on my way home from work when the new cell phone that I had given myself as a Christmas present rang. It was Gary.

"Sanaa," Gary said and then paused.

When he calls me, I know it is serious. We did not often communicate about everyday matters, but I saw him very regularly when I visited Mom because he and his kids were living with her.

"Daddy dead."

There was no easier way for Gary to deliver what was a sad bit of news about our father. Naturally, he was upset at the loss, as he had remained in contact with our father. But it was different for me. I did not know what to feel, as those simple, yet significant words slowly registered in my brain.

Only recently had I allowed myself to think of my father during the few sessions I had had with my life coach. She wanted to know about my relationship with my father when I mentioned that, because of him, I was forced to become almost fully independent since I was 14. That is when it all came out.

For more than 20 years, what I had felt for my father was first resentment and then indifference. I inferred that my homework from the consultation was to try to exorcise the belief my father's abandonment of me had planted in my mind – that I was not good enough. As soon as that process got under way, he was gone. Now my father was truly dead – not only in my heart, but also physically.

"How this happen, Gary?"

"It was sudden ... heart attack."

The occasion of his death was just as I had feared it would be. My father was alone at the time of his death. He was without a close relative around and was found by a church sister, days after his death. That was unsettling.

There was an eerie feeling surrounding me for the first couple of days after I learnt of his death. It is a feeling that I am still unable to convey fully. It felt as if his spirit had travelled more than 120 miles across Jamaica – all the way from the westernmost end of the island, up to the hills of the uppermost part of Kingston, to find me and scold me for having been such a dissenting daughter. Even in death, my father infused me with guilt.

Yet, ironically, his passing would clear the way for me to get to know more about him, and by extension, the rest of my family. For, it was after his death that I spoke to my younger sister, Simone, for the first time. I got her number from Gary, who had seen her on the very day of our father's passing.

It was the beginning of a new chapter in my life.

"Hello Simone, this is Sanaa, your sister," I introduced myself to my own sister. It had to be done and what better time than now?

"Hi, Sanaa, I was planning to call yuh later when I got home. I guess yuh got the news from Gary?"

"Yes," I answered.

When Simone spoke, it was as if I heard an echo of my own voice. She sounded just like me! The more we talked, the weirder it got. She used words I would normally use, paused where I would pause and even seemed to chuckle like I did. My DNA was playing tricks on me and it was a lot to handle.

When we hung up from each other, I wondered if Simone and I looked alike as much as we sounded alike. I thought about the good times she and I had never had together while growing up, and all because of our father's miscalculations. Surely, when we were little girls we could have shared dolls and tried to make dolls' clothes from scraps of fabric left back from my mom's sewing. We could have read the same books and fought as sisters sometimes do. We could have shared secrets about anything that mattered. But, we did not have those memories. Instead, we had one other thing in common aside from our linguistic pattern.

Like my sister, I did not go to my fathers' funeral. We both had excuses, perhaps none of which would have stopped us from attending had he been a different dad. But I can only truly speak for myself.

Were we so angry with him that we wanted to punish him for not loving us enough?

I cannot say.

Still, I was dismayed that I could not even squeeze out a tear when my father died. I felt sad for him though; sad that he had pushed me away so heartlessly and did not even realize how much I had loved him as a child. So, though I did not grieve in the usual way a daughter would be expected to grieve for her father, it was still a solemn time for me.

I recalled how my father used to treat me as a princess when I was a little girl before rejecting me on the cusp of womanhood. He had made me believe that I was no longer worthy of his love and attention because I dared to speak out about matters that were affecting me.

I cut my father's death notice out of the newspaper when it was published. It was in black and white. It had his full name and a picture of him wearing a jacket and necktie. The notice listed the names of all his children, including me. It would be a keepsake – to make up for all the family time I never had with him and my siblings.

In reflecting on my broken relationship with my father, my mind drifted to Brad and our complex relationship over the years. There were clear parallels between my relationship with him and that with my father. I had yearned for their approval of my individuality and for them to fulfil my desires for a conventional family life. The truth is, all that time I had spent pining for their love I lacked the confidence in myself that would have nullified their lack of validation of me.

In Brad's case, I could not deal with the pain of separation, when it was clear there was no future for us. I had sidestepped my conscience to put off our parting, trying to delay that sickening, all too familiar, plunging feeling of rejection that I first experienced when my father forsook me.

Metaphysically, I was suspended in that period of adolescence when I first started believing that I was no good because I had fallen below my father's expectations. Hanging on to any promise of love – no matter how warped – was the only way I knew how to ease the pain. Brad had kept coming back to me each time we parted, offering me temporary reprieve from the pain – giving me that rush that I would get each time he walked back into my life.

As with any drug, the effects never last. The high I got from reuniting with Brad would wear off shortly after his return, leaving me plagued by my insecurities. Brad had played his role in this absurd drama to the hilt, as if he had been performing for an Oscar nomination. Now that I understood not just the script, but also the symbolism of it all, it was time for the final curtain call on that melodramatic period in my life.

I called upon the determination of that girl who had clawed her way back from near failure in high school to become a purposeful and independent woman. In acknowledging my strength, the Universe supported my intentions to stand up confidently and push back against the heaviness of the contrived inadequacies that had weighed me down.

Now that I understood my truth, I could proceed to tidying up my life. I had a new job, but it paid me less than half of what I was previously earning – even though I had higher qualifications. But, this was part of starting over. I was in a new field – market research, in an entry position, almost at the bottom of the ladder, but I was determined to quickly work my way up.

With this clarity, my life had new meaning.

No more time would be wasted fighting for something that was not meant to be. My journey, every little thing I had experienced in my life, brought me to this point of strength. This was the beginning of the rewrite of my life script, where I would play the victor.

While rebuilding my life, I would focus on my son, making sure he would always feel my love and commitment to him.

I was now more appreciative of all my blessings – including the fact of Kai having a sibling, regardless of her being from a different mother. Due to the difficulties I had experienced during my pregnancy, my doctor had cautioned me against having any more children. Having Hannah-Jade in our lives inspired me to take that bold step, reach out, meet and embrace my new siblings – my father's children.

~

This was the beginning of my journey of self-acceptance, of understanding and loving myself, all of who I am – the good and the eccentric. It began with meeting my siblings. They held some of the final pieces to the puzzle about my father.

First, I met Simone, before meeting Lincoln, my brother whose picture had sat so proudly atop the chest of drawers in my father's bedroom. Simone and I spoke several times, after that first call when my father passed, before we met some months later. She came to visit me at home. I went out to the driveway to meet her. Though there was no striking resemblance between us, we recognized each other instantly.

"Wow, you're Simone … you're my sister?" I said.

"Yes!" Simone exclaimed.

We hugged, laughing at the weirdness of what was happening.

We both had seen each other regularly years before, as

we were at university together. We just did not know of our connection then. I do remember though, that when I used to see her on the campus, I always felt that there was something oddly familiar about her, as if I had met her in some other life. She came across as very diligent, with a mission, like me.

It was easy for my sister and me to get to know each other.

With Lincoln, our meeting would take a little longer to materialize. Our initial interaction came just over a year after my father's death, when I gathered the courage to call him. He had left his numbers with Gary for me to call him when I had not shown up at our father's memorial service. Gary had told him that I would reach out when I was ready. At that time, it was a gigantic step for me to take. We had already spent so much of our lifetimes apart and he was living abroad.

Now, having met Simone, it was easier to break down the remaining barrier that my father had erected between us, through his act of non-disclosure.

Getting to know my siblings made me feel as though I had the last triumphant move in what had been like an intensely contested, long, drawn-out chess game between me and my father.

Lincoln and I did not know what to talk about when I first called him, but the conversation eventually flowed.

"Hey Sanaa, you should come visit me and the family in Miami," Lincoln suggested. He was married with two children.

Hmm ... I thought. I had lost count of how many times I had been to that city because of my airline job, but had never taken the initiative to 'link up' with Lincoln. I had been so busy ignoring our father that my brother had become a casualty in the protracted stalemate.

"Ok ..." I said after a brief pause, "Next time I get some vacation, I'll be sure to head your way."

Like our father, Lincoln was a businessman. He sounded authoritative, but without the harsh edge. It felt refreshing to have found such an open older brother, as Gary and I had never developed a close bond.

We continued communicating by telephone until we met two years later. Our conversations were unsurprisingly about our father. I attempted to get some missing infor-mation about my father. I learnt I had been mistaken in my presumption that Lincoln had lived with him while he was growing up.

"Me and the old man weren't close yuh nuh Sanaa. My old lady and him separated when I was very young. I used to live with her in Kingston. I was so sad when she died."

Simone had told me of his mother's tragic death when he was nine years old. She was killed in a car accident. I had asked my mom, years after seeing Lincoln's picture at my father's house, if she knew that my father had other children. She mentioned that she knew of a son. Mom also knew about what had happened to his mother. I was familiar with the story but hearing it from Lincoln was gut wrenching.

"Oh . . . I'm so sorry about that Lincoln," I paused a bit, knowing it was still an emotional moment for him, despite the fact that his mother had passed more than 30 years ago.

"So yuh lived with him after she passed?" I asked.

"When the possibility came up for me to live with him in Mo' Bay I dreaded it. Him was too hard on me, man! I remembered how he would punish me for everything – I couldn't have any friends." "No, no," Lincoln continued hastily. "I got to stay with some of my mother's relatives in Kingston. Even to this day, he never really talked to me about her death."

Lincoln had grieved alone. I imagine that my dad must have felt some amount of grief too, but he did not share that outwardly with his son.

"The following year after she died, he dispatched me to boarding school."

This school was miles away in Mandeville, in the middle of the island, where he knew no one.

Though our dad had ensured that Lincoln got a good education, he was just not emotionally available as a father should have been to a son, to listen to him and coddle him when it mattered most. I found it strange that my mother had taken in so many children unrelated to us over the years, but that Lincoln, having lost his mother, never got the privilege of living with us.

I could not understand why my father had decided a future for Lincoln that had excluded us from his life.

More incredible is the fact that Simone had also experienced the same tragedy. Yes, her mom too had died early in her life, not long after suffering a stroke, when Simone was just entering her teenage years. Like Lincoln, Simone did not have the privilege of coming to live with us, or even spending time with us. My father had never asked my mother to nurture his other children and I wondered why.

You may wonder if my mom would have embraced my father's other offspring. I can assure you that she would have. My kindhearted, selfless and compassionate mother would have, because she never held back from helping anyone.

When I told my mom that I had met Simone, she was surprised to learn that my father had another daughter. For the first time, she revealed that after she had me, she knew little about my father's life, because she had in her words, "cut him off" (and apparently, all other men, because I never ever saw her with a male companion). This was even before she gave her heart to the Lord and was baptized. She was always mindful, however, to allow my father visiting rights.

Simone's fate was that in the last stage of her mother's illness, she was moved to live with our dad's sister in one of the houses he owned in Kingston. It was a nice house, but Simone felt none of the warmth and comfort she had known from being with her mom. She had shelter and food, but she was not feeling any love from her father. What she felt was anxiety whenever he arrived in Kingston and stayed at the house. His very presence would make her feel nervous, because he was exacting.

Simone would automatically brace for a tongue-lashing if, on approaching home from school, she saw our father's car parked in the driveway. She knew she would have to answer to any reported non-compliance with his rules during his absence. One such prohibition was sneaking off to her former home, on her way from school, to see her very ill mother before she finally passed. For some unknown reason, our father had forbidden Simone to visit her mom's home during the weekdays. I do not think she ever forgave him for this insensitivity.

I got the trailer on Simone's life with our father in dribbles, because she still does not like to discuss it. The consistent theme in both Lincoln's and Simone's stories was that generally, living under his jurisdiction was no fun.

Our father had very strict rules for that household. There were three young girls living there: Simone, Fiona – her older sister from her mother's side – and their cousin, Maxine, Uncle Dermott's daughter.

"Simone, Fiona, Maxine!"

"No boys are to come in here!" I don't even want them at my gate! I don't want any teenage pregnancy in this house!"

"Yuh all hear me?"

He did not really expect an answer; only obedience.

Simone had warned all the boys she knew from her church and neighbourhood of his rule and it was easy enough for the young men to comply with it when our father was there. He would be seen sitting on the verandah, puffing on his cigarettes for hours, immersed in his thoughts.

One afternoon, one barefaced young man from the neighbourhood decided that the unwritten 'do not enter' rule was no longer applicable to him.

He pushed the gate, moving in towards the house, even though he saw our father's car parked in the driveway!

Our father was in the shower and had apparently spied the gate crasher approaching from his vantage point of the bathroom window. As the youngster drew closer, and before Simone could caution him, our father came bounding out onto the verandah, a towel tightly draped around his hips, licensed firearm swinging in the direction of the intruder, shouting,

"Yuh think yuh bad eh? Yuh think yuh bad?"

The young man was obviously frightened and not sure what to do.

Our father, still pointing the gun in the direction of the young man, warned him that he was a trespasser. Under the law, our father had the right to shoot him. The overconfident young man immediately lost his bravado. Standing his ground could get him killed, so he bolted in a flash. He spread the word that no one should defy our father's rule, more so, not when he was around.

As you would imagine, our father turned on Simone and duly chastised her for her young friend's lapse in judgement. Of such drama was life with our father.

Lincoln spent time in that home with Simone and our

aunt only for a brief period. After leaving boarding school in Mandeville, he came to live in Kingston while finishing grades 12 and 13. Previously, when he was at boarding school, he would spend his summers with his mom's relatives in Kingston. Lincoln never spent any quality one-on-one time with our father until he was almost an adult. This is when he got the opportunity to see our father more regularly. Of course, even then in the family home, the clashes between father and son continued.

My father's mother, who was sickly for most of her late life, also lived in that family home until she died. She had relocated from the country after her husband, my father's father, had passed. My father never ever took me to his family home. I never met his mother – my own grandmother – or any of his other family members. I wondered if it was deliberate. After all, Gary had eventually met them, but that was when he was older and during the time my father and I were not in touch.

I only met my father's trusted sister after he passed. I could see she was as happy as shocked on meeting me. She stood there, just staring at me, tears rolling down her aged yet smooth cheeks.

After meeting my family members, especially my siblings, I felt that something was not right with the decisions my dad had made about keeping his children apart. In my mind, it deprived us of enriching each other's young lives. I realized that now I would never have the chance to breach my father's *Don't Ask, Don't Tell* policy again; it was too late. He was now dead – gone with all the facts and his groundless philosophies.

A couple of times I had tried to question my mom about this aspect of my life – about the lack of any connection with my father's family. She would skillfully change the subject. I guess her belief was that if you did not speak about something that was unpleasant for you, it would go away with time … not so for me.

None of my father's children knew him well. Not even Gary. None of us had ever been to his place of birth; none of us had any tales of what it was like for him while growing up there.

This is what we knew: he had spent his mid-years in Montego Bay and he had been an upright citizen of his community. There my father had worked hard at his business and had held an honorary position in a service club where he would spend time raising funds for the less fortunate. When with his associates, he switched on the charisma. Perhaps he did not know how to – or no longer cared to banter with his children. His exchanges with us were generally sardonic, always pointing out our failures. I have no idea what had driven my father to lead such a patchwork life. Nor do I understand what led him, in his latter days, to live his life in the highest rectitude – joining the church and avidly studying to become an ordained priest.

Simone believes that he was seeking atonement.

I am not sure if the path to priesthood changed my dad

in any significant way. Maybe this was his way of making peace with himself.

I saw my father once again before he passed. It was for a few hours in his home, years after that ill-fated trip there with Gary. This time it was just us alone – my dad and me.

My old job with the airline often took me to Montego Bay. On one such occasion, while waiting in the airport departure lounge to return to Kingston, I had thought of my father and called him on a whim. We agreed that I would spend some time with him when next I was in his city.

On my next trip to Montego Bay, I made plans to see him. I stayed over with my friend Corinne, who used to work with me at the airport in Kingston. The plan was to spend an entire afternoon with my dad, and I wondered how that would go.

When I saw my father, it seemed as if he had somewhat shrunken in stature. He looked less colossal. The well-dressed man I used to see in my youth – *Sweet Wally*, as Lincoln said they used to call him in his heyday, was gone.

My father was now a retired, almost humbled man. He had not recovered the status that he had lost in the socio-economic debacle of the 1970s, although he had started a new retail business. But his current position in life did not render him less discerning. He had a new yardstick for judging me: The Holy Bible and his new-found religious precepts.

We were sitting at his huge mahogany dining table after

having lunch and talking about nothing in particular, when the subject changed to my personal life.

"Darling," he said, ". . . when are you getting married?"

"Oh, I have been serious with someone for a while," I responded, "but, I'm not sure about marriage."

"Well, San, I hope that you're not living a 'sweetheart life' in Kingston," my father chided as he took a long draw on his cigarette.

I could not believe what I had heard. Did this advice just come from a man who had never given me any guidance when I needed it? It was too late for that at this juncture, I felt. It flashed through my mind that the most helpful thing he had shared with me, after his reappearance in my life, was a proverb.

When Gary and I had visited him in his home he had decided to cook Sunday dinner for us and I had expressed surprise at his culinary skills. My father did not look at me, but he had a cogent response to my comment as he lowered the steak into the sizzling oil in the waiting Dutch pot.

"Darling, remember this," my father said, "it is always better to light a candle than to curse the dark."

This was good advice, which I had always lived by because of my mother's example of how to manage in trying times. I filed his wise axiom in the back of my head, but I thought it was too bad that he had not been around to give me such well-needed guidance throughout my youth.

This time though, I decided to take the route I had

taken many years ago, except that now it was like a game for me – that of pointedly asking him about a matter he would not choose to discuss voluntarily. I was never able to handle his responses in the past. How would I fare now?

"I didn't realize you were still smoking," I said, "considering you are now converted, plus the fact that it is not good for your health."

"Darling, it's not what goes into the mouth but what comes out of it that defiles it," my father quoted this memory gem placidly from his new reference book, the Bible.

Well, there I was questioning his actions once again, but this was his softest comeback yet. I could see that my father felt absolved of any need to justify himself to me, having found such a precise Bible verse to counter my tactlessness. Obviously, I had not learnt my 'don't ask' lesson over the years and I could tell I was still failing miserably in his sight. Yet, at that moment, I believe my father also felt some regret for not knowing me more in his days of strength, but he was still a little too proud to tell me.

I left my father's house that evening thinking that maybe he was not as unfeeling as he had depicted himself.

That was the last time my father and I saw each other. I went to Montego Bay many times after that visit, but I never ever called him again. And he never met his grandson, Kai. He heard about him from Gary. Kai often asked me,

"Mommy, why didn't you ever take me to see Grandpa Wallenston?"

I had no straight answer to give him, as there was no

justifiable excuse. I was guilty of some of the same errors of omission my father had made.

The truth is, having failed to regain my father's love, I did not want to face his constant judgement on my life. I could never please him. I could only hope that one day he would forgive me for not meeting his expectations.

epilogue

Taking the Boldest Steps

Now you know my story and the story of how I lost my father, met my new siblings and found myself.

Since meeting my siblings, I have filled in most, if not all the missing pieces of the puzzle of my father's life – and my own life too. My new siblings and I will remain connected because of our father. Just trying to uncover his mystery is enough to bind us together. One thing we know for sure is that we have all inherited his tenacity.

I can see bits and pieces of my enigmatic father in each of us. We all have a wisp of his pensiveness lodged in our souls, but we also have his perseverance to fight back regardless of the odds and to rise above our misfortunes and move beyond our mistakes.

Now that I know my family ties and understand my genetic make-up – that which makes me unique – I have learned the real lesson I needed to learn from the first time I had lost my father: I should always reject labels that limit me. And so, I am discovering the joys of unconditional self-love, the reassuring love that releases me from worrying about not being enough for others. Deliberately confronting my unfounded fears of inadequacy has lifted the fog of self-doubt that stunted me since I was 14 years old.

I am embracing every aspect of myself, past and present, and now appreciate who I am, with all my quirks. And, I have realized after all these years, that I did not have to be ashamed or feel less important because my father chose not to be a part of my life. None of this was about my own shortcomings. Yet, for many years, I thought I was just not good enough.

I am now on the journey of self-improvement – not in pursuit of perfection, but to become a better and more confident person. It's an intricate process and sometimes I do falter, but I learn and move forward.

As for Brad and me, we finally parted shortly after my father passed. We have found some amount of equilibrium that allows us to jointly parent our son, and so, our lives have remained intertwined. Kai stayed with Brad after I moved out, as I was still in my transition to stability.

Neither Brad nor I can deny that we once shared an intense love, but it was tumultuous, as he had a different outlook on love and family. However, I should only speak for myself on certain matters. What I can say for sure is that my preconceived beliefs of what love, and especially family, should look like, have been challenged and have fallen to pieces before my eyes. These days, I am in love with life and the opportunity it brings each day for renewal.

And what of my country? We have come a very long way since the 1970s.

When P.J. Patterson retired in 2006 before his term ended, Jamaica welcomed its first female prime minister – Portia Simpson-Miller – affectionately called "Sister P"

Patterson was satisfied he had left a legacy. He had kept the PNP in power for 15 years, winning three successive elections, keeping Seaga and the JLP at bay election after election. His strategy for bringing about the well-needed reform of Jamaica's electoral system resulted in the establishment of the Electoral Commission of Jamaica in 2006. The commission's job primarily entailed creating a system that could safeguard the democratic process in Jamaica. But Patterson was not able to eliminate Jamaica's social ills, crime and corruption, even after 15 years.

A lot of hope was now vested in Sister P. Could she confront the Gorgons of poverty, crime and corruption?

Sister P had been a Vice President of the PNP since 1978. She had contested P.J. Patterson for party leadership when Michael Manley was bowing out in 1989. Jamaica was not ready for a female leader at that time, but her popularity had been growing since then.

Sister P's rise to power was spectacular on two accounts. First as a woman and second, she did not have an Ivy League education as did her immediate predecessors in the PNP. She was not from a sophisticated background, but she had worked her way up through the ranks of representational politics to become the most popular leader in her party. Even persons outside of the PNP were backing Sister P as she spoke openly about her love for, and dedication to the poor throughout her campaign for leadership prior to P.J.'s departure.

No one had to ask who Sister P was. She stood out in a crowd. She was statuesque and had a special charm. Sister P was approaching 70 when she geared up to take on the highest political office, but her energy belied this fact.

Whenever you saw her on TV at the PNP campaign rallies, she was always prancing – jumping, knees high – sometimes running from side to side on the stage, as she shouted her love for serving her party and her people. Between these sentiments of love, she threw barbs at the JLP about how long they were in opposition and reminded them that they had 'mashed up' the country in the 1980s. The look in her eyes was like that of a preacher of the gospel – spirit-filled and charged with telling the Good News.

If you were ever lucky to spot Sister P arriving at a more formal public function she would be composed, walking briskly into the room, head high, shoulders back and commanding instant respect. You could easily single out Sister P from among her comrades. She was always well coiffed, tastefully dressed in a designer suit and wearing her Ray Ban shades as if they could screen her stateliness.

Soon the crowd would swallow her up no matter how hard her personal guards tried to protect her from the many who wanted to get a touch or a hug from Sister P. She may have been from among the poor, but Sister P's confident carriage conveyed to us her conviction that she was destined to lead Jamaica. She was particularly popular among the poor, for whom she professed much love. And they often pledge their allegiance to her on the popular radio talk shows and in their letters to newspaper editors.

One ardent supporter wrote:

The Editor, Sir:

I wish to state categorically that it is time for a grassroots leader to be our prime minister. The best candidate is none other than Portia Simpson-Miller. She is for the people, by the people and of the people. She is a true representative for the poor as she herself has come from a poor, rural community. She has been fighting our cause in parliament since 1976, and it is time to give her a chance to lead us and turn this country around. Tell me Mr Editor, who else is more deserving of becoming the next PNP president and prime minister of Jamaica than our real, real grassroots leader, Portia Simpson-Miller?

Sincerely,

Gussie Stokes

And who could blame Sister P's followers for wanting to put someone like themselves – someone in touch with their plight – in the highest political office?

Gussie Stokes got his wish.

Not long after his letter to the editor of *The Gleaner,* in 2006, Patterson left the PNP in the hands of Sister P. She emerged as winner from among the VPs – beating out not one, or two but three scholarly male counterparts who had vied for the post of PNP Party Leader.

It was "woman time now", the people said.

Sister P's headship of state in 2006 was a warm and fuzzy moment in our political history. She showered all of us – particularly the poor – with speeches that focused on love, as much as they did on fixing the country.

Sister P also spent time becoming acquainted with her international and regional political peers. One such was Hugo Chavez, from Venezuela. Her rapport with Chavez was easy – he and the PNP shared similar socialist philosophies. More importantly, Jamaica and Venezuela had an excellent diplomatic relationship that dated back many decades. In 2005, the year before Sister P came into office, Jamaica and Venezuela had signed the PetroCaribe Energy Cooperation Agreement. This arrangement was spearheaded by Chavez; it allowed Jamaica (and other poor regional island states who also signed on), to purchase oil from Venezuela without paying the full cost up-front. Jamaica would pay back the monies for the oil over a 25-year period, at a minimal interest rate of one percent (under certain conditions). And we could also repay part of this debt with goods or services. The proceeds from local oil sales would be invested by the PetroCaribe Development Fund established in 2006.

The deal was brilliant – particularly the establishment of the Fund, which would provide financing for development projects. However, this sort of arrangement was too technical for grassroots appreciation. The JLP Opposition saw it as a 'sell out' to Venezuela. On top of that, people were complaining that they weren't ". . . feeling Sister P."

Crime was still high, and corruption was still rampant. And although inflation had plummeted, reaching a record single-digit low of 5.8 percent between 2006 and 2007, this was not enough to ease the plight of the poor after Sister P took leadership of the country.

Understandably – two years was not enough time for Sister P to effect much change during this interim tenure; she needed a full five-year term – one with her own mandate. However, there was one problem; allegations surfaced before the upcoming elections that her party had taken contributions from an unauthorized source. Would this mar her chances of winning?

Sister P remained silent on the matter.

At the end of her interim term in office, when the PNP's official five-year term was over and the elections were called, Sister P lost to Bruce Golding and the JLP.

Finally, the JLP would taste power again, after many years in the political wilderness. Bruce had received the forgiveness of Labourites of all persuasion, as well as those who funded the party's election campaign. With Seaga out, he had successfully challenged the PNP. The message taken from the slim margin of victory for the JLP was that, despite the mutual love between the people and Sister P, the PNP had been in office for a little too long (18 uninterrupted years).

While Portia Simpson-Miller ruminated on the 2007 election results, Bruce Golding was ushered in as the new Prime Minister of Jamaica.

As soon as he took office, Bruce Golding introduced numerous changes to initiate his campaign promises. They came fast. First, he addressed some social issues by removing fees for accessing public health services and removing some miscellaneous charges for students studying at the secondary education level. Next, he made some ceremonial changes to his title to prove he was a different type of politician. He dropped the 'Most' from his official title 'Most Honourable Bruce Golding' and from those of all JLP ministers; perhaps to warm up to his Jamaican people.

Most important, he also agreed with the PNP Opposition Party in 2008 that it was time to work together to fix the country's social ills through bipartisanship. This is how the Partnership for Transformation Programme was conceptualized and initiated. Its main stakeholders were the private sector, the government, other interest groups representing non-governmental organizations and civil society, indeed, all citizens of Jamaica. In this Partnership, Jamaican politicians and all Jamaicans would need to demonstrate to each other the willingness to promote necessary changes in our society.

Even more commendable for both parties was the introduction of the *Vision 2030 Jamaica – National Development Plan,* a roadmap developed by the country's official planning agency to help Jamaica achieve First World status by 2030. With this Plan, by 2030, the country should achieve higher global ranking in overall quality of life as "… the choice of place to live, work, raise families and do business". The overarching aim was people empowerment and economic prosperity.

Having implemented a raft of changes, Bruce Golding felt confident, as the end of his first term approached, that there was a high probability Jamaicans would give him a second term – something the JLP had not achieved in recent times.

However, just at that time, news broke that Jamaica was in trouble with the United States of America.

America had made an extradition request for a member of the prime minister's constituency, Tivoli Gardens, an inner-city community in western Kingston. The allegation was that this individual had committed crimes against America. Bruce Golding had not complied, instead seeking legal advice on how to circumvent the request. Uncle Sam was getting impatient. People were in disbelief on hearing the news.

"What?"

"Wasn't Bruce the new promoter for good governance?"

"Didn't he promise to rid the country of crime and corruption?"

"Why would he protect a don?"

Residents in the Tivoli community knew this individual; he was like their godfather – only doing good in their eyes. Apparently, the Americans thought otherwise. They wanted him to be tried on their own soil, in their courts.

This put Prime Minister Golding in a sticky position. He was caught between community loyalty, and both legal and moral obligation. How was he going to detach himself from this situation? How was he to make a decision that would extradite a man who had kept his constituency, Tivoli Gardens, safe? The situation was challenging.

When the prime minister finally decided to grant the US government's request after public outcry, the security forces were sent into Tivoli to retrieve the don. But the community members mounted defences against the security forces. The don was untouchable and the community members were prepared to protect him with their lives.

There was mayhem in West Kingston, the likes of which Jamaicans had not seen for a long time. Although the war was mostly confined to that region, the entire country was gripped by fear, especially when a police station in neighbouring Denham Town, was set ablaze. This was considered an attack on the state itself.

Those on the frontline of defence fought desperately and many lost their lives. To manage the insurrection, the government had to impose a state of emergency in the area.

It was May 2010, but the Tivoli Incursion, as it was later called, was like a flashback to the 1970s – it resembled the upheaval in political violence of those times. Except, this time, the war was between the citizens of the community and the state.

This served as a turning point for us. We would no longer tolerate excuses from our leaders for not standing up against wrongdoing. Political indiscretion was under the spotlight.

Bruce Golding caved under the pressure of the criticisms and demitted office before his term ended.

If the JLP wanted to win the next election, they would have to find someone without 'baggage'; someone who would be attractive to the masses – particularly the young who were apathetic about politics and hence, not engaged in the political process. But, such a person would have to face Portia Simpson Miller once again, as she had remained the leader of the PNP and the favoured leader among the poor.

Jamaicans had no indication which way the election would go.

The one thing we were sure of was that we wanted leaders who were prepared to do the right thing at the right time, to staunchly protect the rule of law. The question was,

"Who should we trust?"

I will be sure to keep my eye on them and will get back to you soon.

In the meantime, if you should ever get a chance to speak with any of our current or aspiring leaders, please feel free to share my story with them. Tell them that only when I broke free from thinking that I was not enough, did I really begin to live triumphantly.

Also, tell them that I learnt that covering up the truth about what caused my mistakes and hurts, or blaming others for them, would not move me forward. I remained stuck until I learnt the lesson the Universe was trying to teach me.

Lastly and most important, I would ask you to leave them with the impassioned words of Mikhail Gorbachev, one who was brave enough to lead change in his time, within his party, his government, his country and indeed the world.

"We have come to see that half-hearted measures will not work here. We must act on a wide front, consistently and energetically, without failing to take the boldest steps."

I do not want to sound sanctimonious here – you know I am no saint. However, I believe that the most important task ahead of us is not accepting a half-hearted approach to governance, or anything else that matters to us in life. After all, as a people we pride ourselves in winning – even against the odds. Our bobsled team is testament to our fortitude, competing daringly in the Olympic Winter Games over the years. Who, on seeing them perform, would believe that they come from a tropical country?

Certainly, for me, trying to forget about my father by pretending that he did not exist did not change my identity or his legacy to me. Instead, it got me stuck in a wilderness where I lived as a victim of my own feelings of inadequacy – planted when my father took his love away from me. Only the deliberate action of purging myself through self-reconciliation and forgiving my father released me from that valley. Accepting my truth has liberated me, allowing me to enjoy the abundant life that I deserve. No more 'smalling up' of myself in that overcrowded valley of self-denial.

I have no doubt that this renewed perspective will shape the next spellbinding chapters of my life. It will include how I met my other new sister, last Christmas.

In the meantime, I am heading off to Calabash, Jamaica's literary festival. There I am going to take the open microphone. I plan to share one of my poems I once thought was silly – titled "Labels Just Don't Fit" – to a crowd of complete strangers who have no idea that I used to be afraid of sharing the words I put on paper. I'm not sure how they will react. But for me, reading my writing out loud will be the boldest step I have taken in a very long while.

Made in the USA
Columbia, SC
01 November 2019